PELICAN BOOKS

A 449

APPLIED GEOGRAPHY

L. DUDLEY STAMP

L. Dudley Stamp was born in London in 1898 and educated at King's College where he graduated with First Class Honours in Geology, following this by an M.Sc. and later by a B.A. First Class Honours in Geography. After service in the First World War with the Artists' Rifles and Royal Engineers he spent three years exploring for oil and minerals in Burma and at the age of twenty-five was appointed the first Professor of Geology and Geography in the University of Rangoon. Returning to England in 1926 he was for nearly twenty years Sir Ernest Cassel Reader in Economic Geography at the London School of Economics, before becoming Professor of Geography in 1945, and Professor of Social Geography from 1948 to 1958. During those years he organized in the nineteen-thirties the Land Utilisation Survey of Britain. He has been President of the Geographical Association and of the Institute of British Geographers, and from 1952 to 1956 served as President of the International Geographical Union. He was a Member of the Royal Commission on Common Land (1955–7). He was awarded the C.B.E. in 1946, and holds honorary doctorates from the Universities of Clark, U.S.A. (1955), Stockholm (1959), Warsaw (1962), and Edinburgh (1963). He is currently President of the Royal Geographical Society.

Penguin Books Ltd, Harmondsworth, Middlesex, England
Penguin Books Inc., 3300 Clipper Mill Road, Baltimore 11, Md, U.S.A.
Penguin Books Pty Ltd, Ringwood, Victoria, Australia

—

First published 1960
Reprinted, with Notes on Further Reading, 1961
Reprinted, with minor corrections, 1963
Reprinted 1964

—

—

Made and printed in Great Britain
by Richard Clay & Company, Ltd, Bungay, Suffolk
Set in Monotype Baskerville

CONTENTS

LIST OF TEXT FIGURES

7

List of Text Figures

CHAPTER I

The Meaning and Scope of Applied Geography

THE first half of this century has seen the emergence of the modern study of geography as an academic discipline fit to take its place among the older disciplines of science, the social sciences, and the liberal arts in every university of Britain. This remarkable and rapid growth, paralleled by that of the study of geography at all levels in schools, is undoubtedly due to the realization that there is an intimate relationship between man and his environment and that no other subject seeks to understand or interpret this relationship in its entirety both in space and time. The field is vast, and it is not surprising that this holistic view of human ecology should sometimes be in danger of degenerating into superficial knowledge with facile correlations. It is obvious, too, that research in geography must either be achieved by limitation of area – the intensive study of all the factors in a small region – or limitation of field to part only of the environment or its influence, or to a definite and brief period of time such as the present. But undoubtedly the unique contribution of the geographer is the holistic approach in which he sees the relationship between man and his environment, with its attendant problems, as a whole. This he must achieve by first-hand investigations, by survey in the field, and the gathering of facts systematically and objectively, at the same time using the results obtained by many specialists into whose fields he is neither equipped nor required to enter personally, but without whose findings his own picture would be incomplete. Such is the geographical method of survey and analysis.

But both are achieved fully only when studied cartographically. One is tempted to recall such comments, trite but true, as 'the map is the tool of the geographer' or 'geography is the study of distributions'. It is in the representation of data on maps and their interpretation or cartographic analysis that the geographer makes his unique contribution to a team investigation. A body of original data can be analysed in several ways. Usually it can be analysed statistically, usually it can be analysed cartographically, and the two analyses are complementary. A good example is afforded by the Farm Survey which the British Ministry of Agriculture undertook in the early years of the Second World War. An extensive and detailed questionnaire was filled in for every one of the 300,000 odd farmers in England and Wales, and a map prepared of each farm. When the results were analysed statistically it could be shown that 53 per cent of farms were without a piped water supply and that only 27 per cent had electric light and power. It is only, however, when the farms without piped water supply are plotted on maps that a particular pattern of distribution is apparent: only when that pattern is studied in relation to other distribution patterns can one trace the influence of such factors as rainfall, drainage, accessibility, poverty of land, or area of local government.

Similarly, a farm holding can be recorded as 'fragmented', but only when the farm map is compared with maps of relief, drainage, soil, and microclimate does it become apparent whether the fragmentation is justified by physical conditions or is merely the result of historical accidents.

If the past fifty years have been spent in developing geographical methods of survey and analysis, surely the time has now come to apply those methods towards the understanding and interpretation of some of the features of the world of today. Further, the time has surely come when those same methods of survey and analysis can be used in helping towards the solution of some of the great world problems – the increasing pressure of population on space, the development of under-developed areas, or the attempt to improve living conditions, which is the object of town and country planning. Such is, indeed, the field of applied geography, and in the pages which follow a number of current problems will be examined and subjected to geographical analysis.

For many years past this has been my own special field of work and interest. My title as Professor of Social Geography in the University of London was to some extent an accident. When it was proposed, in the years following the Second World War, to establish a Chair in the University to further the development of geographical studies which would assist in unravelling the innumerable problems by which we are surrounded, it was felt by the sponsors to be so closely related to the range of the Social Sciences that the title should be Professor of Social Geography rather than Professor of Applied Geography. But the scope and content were not changed thereby, except that in studying applied geography one is constantly reminded that the applications one seeks are for the benefit of society.

The scope of applied geography is world wide, but in order to keep this book within manageable proportions it has been deliberately restricted, except for a few points, to the British Isles.

CHAPTER 2

The Human Environment

IF the essential concept of geography is the study of the earth as the home of man, or the study of man's environment, what are the chief factors which make up that environment? In other words, if we look upon the earth as the stage on which the drama of human life is played, what are the features of that stage which need to be separated and studied? The theoretical picture of the environment and its influence on man is broadly the same whether we are considering an individual or a nation, a single homestead, a region, or a country. We can split the environment into its component though closely related parts and analyse the influence of each of the factors thus separated.

The first factor of the environment is location. We can express this in absolute terms of latitude and longitude relative to the earth's surface as a whole: we can, and more commonly do, express it in relation to the obvious and fixed points on the earth's surface. We can say, for example, that a man resides in a house situated in Lat. 51° 29′ 30″ N. and Long. 1° 3′ 15″ W., or we can say he resides on the western margin of the small town of X in the county of Y in southern England. In any case his daily activities are largely influenced by the location of his home. The space relationship between his home and his place of work determine the hour at which he rises in the morning and departs for work. The location of his home gives him certain neighbours, and the propinquity has certain consequences. Similarly with a country: we can express its area in square miles or square kilometres, we can say it stretches through certain degrees of latitude and longitude. This fixes its position on the earth's surface; it also gives it certain fixed relationships with regard to seas and oceans, to climatic regions, and notably to its neighbours. Much time and thought have been given, by individuals and nations, to counteracting the dominant influence of location. One aspect of this struggle is the attempt to conquer distance. Man, who once walked four miles an hour, later tamed the horse to carry him at ten, and developed the railway engine to take him at sixty, now commonly uses a plane which cruises at 300 miles an hour. No part of the world is now theoretically more than a day's journey from any other part. In so far as communication of thought and word is concerned, the disadvantages of location have been overcome to such an extent that by radio communication is instantaneous over the whole earth. On the other hand, we remain unable to move the actual lands and seas. It might be an advantage, climatically and politically, to tow the British Isles to a new location in the middle of the North Atlantic Ocean: it cannot be done. How many nations would be grateful to be relieved of frontier problems and of neighbours they do not desire! Although we must thus accept location as fixed and inevitable, history abounds with examples, often successful, of moving peoples with all their attendant activities from one location to another.

The second factor of the environment we may call the factor of physical relief – the form of the land surface. If a man has a house on a hill he must needs climb to it: the activities of a whole country are conditioned by the build of the land, whether mountain, hill, or plain. The basic problem of Japan is that only a seventh of the land surface is comprised of plains or gentler slopes which can be cultivated. One cannot, as yet, take a steam-roller or a bulldozer and turn the hilly land of Wales into an East Anglian plain. On a relatively small scale man's conquest of the relief of the land has made vast strides in recent years. The canal era, and especially the railway era, saw the piercing of hills and even of great mountain ranges by tunnels: roads continued to wind over hill and dale till modern earth-moving machinery made possible economically what unaided human labour could scarcely accomplish. Physical environment is overcome also in other ways, notably in drainage and reclamation. Nevertheless the fact remains that the relief of the land is a dominant factor in the life and economic development of a country. It is for this reason that such standard atlases as *The Times* use essentially layer-coloured or relief maps. They at once give some indication of the potential value of the land which a map using plain colours for political divisions does not.

The relief of the land is but the outward and visible result of the underlying geological structure and of vast ages of evolution of surface forms. Hence a third factor of the environment is the structure of the earth's crust. It has many effects, both direct and indirect, on the life of man and nature. The harder or more resistant rocks tend to remain as upstanding masses of hills and mountains, the softer or less resistant to form plains and valleys. The former tend to be associated with poor soils, the latter with richer soils more conducive to cultivation. We can indeed divide Britain on this basis roughly into Highland Britain of the north and west, Lowland Britain of the south and east. In the second place geological structure controls the distribution of rocks and minerals. Minerals of economic importance may lie deeply hidden and demand all the resources of modern man to detect them before they can be exploited, but the simple fact remains – no mineral deposit can be located where it has not already been placed by Nature. In their mineral resources Nature has drawn her own distinction between the 'haves' and the 'have nots': in consequence this is a factor of utmost importance.

More especially of recent years it has been realized that the development of the detail of a land surface – such as the existence of a flat-topped hill there, or a bench on a valley-side there, or a sudden break of slope, or a succession of riverside terraces – may be the result of a long and very complicated interaction of forces. The attempt to unravel the story has given rise to the specialized study known as geomorphology – the study of earth forms. The details of earth form have often been of greatest importance in the life of man; London, for example, owes its site originally to the existence of two gravel-capped low hills bordering the river but free from flooding.

Whilst the supply of water is derived largely from rainfall and surface streams, the underground geological structure determines the existence of aquifers or rocks holding an underground supply, and of the position and character of springs. Many of our villages were sited originally where there was an assured water supply from a spring. Almost equally important is the influence of geology on drainage, and so on agriculture and other aspects of land use. Clays hold up water on the surface, sands and sandstones permit it to seep slowly downwards, coarse sands or fissured rocks may cause surface water to be drained away too quickly.

Few factors of the environment impinge more directly on our daily lives than weather and climate. The weather from day to day dictates the clothes we elect to wear: almost every day we use our own judgement as weather prophets in this regard. Climate determines in a large measure the building of our homes, and especially the provision of means of heating them: it is obvious that climate dictates the range of crops which a country can economically produce and so, indirectly, the range of primary commodities which that country must import if it wishes to maintain a full life in the modern sense. The elements of weather and climate which are of significance are several. Temperature and precipitation (rain, hail, and snow) are fundamental, but evaporation, frost, wind, dew, mist, and fog each may exercise its influence.

As we have already noted, climate through rainfall dominates the water-supply position, but it is not always realized that we owe our soils as much to climate as we do to the nature of the underlying rocks. Soil science or pedology has become in recent years a complex study of its own.

An uninhabited area of the earth's surface would be covered by a mantle of natural vegetation. In the main it would depend on climatic conditions – temperature and moisture – and so it would constitute what the botanist would call the climatic climax. The mantle would be interrupted at intervals where soil conditions – rock outcrops or water-logging – prevented the development of such a climax, and one would find instead an edaphic or soil climax. In fact, however, there are very few parts of the world where the strictly 'natural' vegetation remains. Nearly everywhere there is evidence of the hand of man. Where men have cleared the forest or ploughed the prairie this is obvious, it is perhaps less marked where human influence is exercised indirectly through grazing animals or through forest and grassland fires. The greater part of the vegetation cover, where the land is not actually cultivated, can best be described as 'semi-natural'. It follows that a careful survey of existing vegetation, natural and semi-natural, especially if combined with a survey of the areas actually cultivated or farmed, will afford a remarkable picture which, if properly interpreted, reveals not only the influence of all the natural factors of relief, soil, climate, drainage, but also the results of human activity. This is the purpose behind land-use surveys, which will be discussed in detail later. Just as types of vegetation may thus be used as 'indicators' of potential quality and fertility of land, so individual plants can be used as 'plant indicators'. A good land agent assessing the value of an estate knows well how the form of a tree gives him a good index of the quality of the land.

Just as the major factor influencing the development of natural vegetation is climate, so climate is the major factor influencing the possible cultivation of crops selected by man to satisfy his needs. Types of farming are thus linked closely with climate, and this introduces the whole field of agricultural geography. An interesting point may be mentioned here. It is possible, in most cases, to draw ultimate or geographical limits for the cultivation of a given crop. There are parts of Britain, for example, which lie beyond the limits in the case of the vine, maize, wheat, and even barley. Near the margins crops may fail in one season out of two or three. But Nature is perverse and often rewards the adventurous who farm near the margin by crops of exceptional quality and quantity in favoured years. Moreover, it is the constant aim of agricultural science to extend the limits for crops by developing strains resistant to cold or drought or excessive moisture. Where economic forces or incentives are sufficiently strong adverse climatic conditions may be overcome by irrigation, pest control, and other means.

If man's life is influenced by the natural vegetation cover of the earth's surface, it is also influenced by the fauna often intimately associated with the flora. Lions and tigers may still be a menace occasionally: deaths from snake-bite are still numerous in some countries, but over vast areas man has killed off the larger animals or induced them to live harmlessly in national parks. True, the rabbit menace remained in Britain to destroy annually a considerable proportion of farm crops till myxomatosis swept the country and altered the whole balance of Nature. Man's struggle is rather with the smaller creatures – the plagues of locusts, the swarms of mosquitoes, or the amoeba spreading dysentery – but there also the spread of man's control in recent years has been remarkable. There is, however, a wide and fascinating field of medical geography, and much work remains to be done not only in the careful mapping of regions subject to different diseases and pests, but also in the study of the environmental factors.

In sum all these are factors of the environment which singly and collectively exercise a varying influence on the life of man. In the past, the term 'geographical control' was used, and some extremists went so far as to assert that the control was so strong as to determine the whole course of human existence. 'Determinism' makes no allowance for the accidents of history which have so often played a major role: the word does not recognize the power of man to fight against and to overcome the obstacles raised by his environment. We do better always to think of the influence of the environmental factors and of the reciprocal influence of man on the operation of those factors – even to their complete elimination in some cases. In the words of Athelston Spilhaus, 'one essential difference between man and the lesser animals is that man strives to change his environment to meet his peculiar needs, whereas other forms of life in the course of time submissively adapt themselves to the whims of their surroundings.' This view may be expressed by the following simple diagram.

This diagram suggests the complex environment. Any part of that environment is a legitimate sphere of study for a geographer and he may indeed restrict his researches accordingly. In the diagram I have simply recorded the central

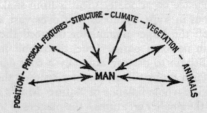

Fig. 1. The relationship between man and his environment

figure as man. Clearly, however, we may consider either as a whole or separately the many phases of human activity – social, economic, political. There is no difficulty in seeing what is meant by population geography, economic geography, industrial geography, agricultural geography, and so on. The field may be narrowed, as in transport geography, or even pin-pointed, as in the geography of malaria. Treated as a whole, we may apply the scheme in the diagram to a single country or even to a region within a country. Such is regional geography. But the basic concept is equally applicable to a single settlement: intensively studied, we have urban geography.

So far we have talked of space and said nothing of time. The relationship between man and his environment is ever changing: it is essentially dynamic and never static. One aspect of historical geography is the study of the relationship at given times in the past: another aspect of historical geography is to trace the changes from past to present. It may be categorically stated that it is never safe to deduce relationships from the present alone: it is vital to see the present as a stage in a natural process of evolution. We see the establishment of trends which, other factors remaining as at present, can be projected into the future. Here we see the vital link between geography and physical planning. For planning consists essentially of deliberately encouraging trends which are accounted to be good, or of countering those believed to be bad. The easier way is to work with Nature, using the natural influence of the environment, wherever possible. Only with a proper understanding, therefore, of environmental influences can physical planning, national or local, hope to succeed. At this stage the objective survey and analysis of the geographer passes into the subjective judgement of the planner. Planning presupposes a policy, and policy may be based on considerations far removed from the geographic. Just as in many branches of science the 'pure' scientist considers himself concerned only in the search for new knowledge and is content, or indeed prefers, to leave to others the application of his discoveries, so the geographer may consider his work ends with survey and analysis. But, if he chooses to follow up his findings logically to their application, his subjective judgement is certainly deserving of full consideration.

It is often urged that, however important limiting physical conditions may have been in the past, advances in technology have rendered them, or are rendering them, of less account. Broadly speaking, the reverse is true. In the past, with indifferent means of transport or communications, the village, the county, or the country lived relatively self-contained lives. If the people wanted wheaten bread, they had to grow the wheat, even though physical conditions were far from favourable. Today sees a world of marked areal specialization: it is rarely economic to cultivate a crop or produce a commodity where physical environmental conditions are unfavourable. The general trend towards a free-trade world, where every region produces those commodities for which it is best fitted by Nature, is hindered only by such man-made barriers as tariffs and trade restrictions.

CHAPTER 3

Land and People

In a world beset by innumerable immediate problems, one long-range problem stands out above all others. It is the rapidly increasing pressure of population on land resources. The world's people are unevenly distributed over the land surface, so that whilst in some countries – e.g. Japan – population pressure is the dominant problem, in others – e.g. the United States – it is sufficiently far from being a dominant problem to be difficult of comprehension. In Britain it is definitely in the forefront and has led directly to the comprehensive system of town and country planning under which we have been working since the passing of the Act of 1947.

Whilst the land surface of the earth may seem enormous – it is about 55,786,000 square miles, or 35,703,040,000 acres, against a water surface of 141,050,000 square miles or 90,272 million acres – it is definite, finite, and broadly speaking inextensible. There are no vast new lands waiting to be discovered, as there were even as recently as a couple of hundred years ago, and every year our knowledge of the exact area and character of the lands, even remote Antarctica, becomes more exact. By comparison with the whole, the land which can be added by reclamation is tiny in total area and we may therefore take the land of the earth as fixed in extent.

But what of the people? Because knowledge and practice of death control – the ever-increasing control or even elimination of disease and the consequent extension of human life – have overtaken the knowledge and practice of birth control, the human family is increasing more rapidly than ever before in the history of the earth. It is now possible to state, with a margin of error of not more than perhaps 2 or 3 per cent, what is the present population of the world.

With the carrying out of a census on modern lines in China in 1953 the last of the great unknown factors was eliminated. And so we can say, with reference to mid-1964, that the world's population was of the order of 3,220 million people.

It is not so much this figure, staggering and incomprehensible as it may be, which is a world concern as the rate of increase. The total is certainly double what it was fifty years ago, and the best estimates of present increase are of the order of 2·0 per cent per annum. This is *net* increase, not birth rate, which is between 3 and 4 per cent per annum.

Authoritative figures are published annually by the United Nations Organization in the *Demographic Yearbook*, and the estimated net increase for the year 1962–3 was over 60 million. Thus the world adds unto itself in that one year a population three times that of the whole of Canada, or more than five times that of Australia. Over a single span of twenty-four hours the world adds to itself a population equivalent to that of a city of 170,000 – say Blackpool or Middlesbrough or Bournemouth. Put in another way, about five babies are born every second of every day, and the net increase is nearly two a second.

At present the distribution of population over the earth's surface is very uneven. It naturally bears some relationship to the capacity of different regions to support population and to those climates where life is relatively easy, but even so some lands carry a population far below their potential, whilst others, in this sense, are definitely over-populated and could not keep alive their people on home food production alone. We must of course repeat, *in this sense*, because industrial regions are naturally food-deficit regions and an industrial country such as Britain cannot automatically be called over-populated because it cannot feed itself.

The relationship between land and people can be studied on at least four levels. The first is the world level: the capacity of the world as a whole to support the growing population. Whilst this offers some fascinating fields of speculation, it is, in fact, a somewhat academic approach so long as there exist the innumerable man-made barriers which prevent free movement of men and materials.

A more realistic approach is at the second level – the national level – and this affords some remarkable contrasts between one country and another.

Especially within the larger national units – one thinks, for example, of Brazil or Australia – there are often extreme contrasts between one region of a country and another, and this affords a third level of study – the regional level.

The local relationships between land and people bring us into the sphere of town planning, or country planning in the British sense, where the unit is a single county, and so to the pin-point relationship between an individual settlement and the geographical environment – for example, the productive capacity of a single farm or the possibility for a single family to wrest an adequate living from a small holding.

Taking first the world position, it may be stated that the average population density over the whole land surface is at present about fifty-six persons per square mile or twenty-two persons per square kilometre. Although this is the commonest and most usual way of expressing density, I find it simpler to think in terms of land per person or head of population.

If the land surface of the globe were divided up equally, the share falling to each person, man, woman, and child, would be roughly 11 acres. But this would include a slice of the frozen wastes of Antarctica, a section of the burning sands of the Sahara, a share of the equatorial forests of the Amazon or Congo, and of the rocky slopes of the Himalayas. The concept has been revived in recent years of the *oecumene* or *ecumene* – the habitable earth: those parts of the earth's surface which are capable of permanent settlement and development to produce human food. With this concept in mind we may eliminate about a fifth of the total surface as being too cold to support permanent settlement in this way – the vast continent of Antarctica, of some 4,411,000 square miles, as well as most of Greenland, and so on. Another fifth can be eliminated as too arid and having no water supplies available. Another fifth is too elevated, too mountainous or rugged. Perhaps another tenth is bare rock or lacking soil which could adequately support crop growth. So the potentially cultivable area, the oecumene, is seen to be some 30 per cent only of the whole, and the 11 acres per head of population is reduced to about $3\frac{1}{2}$ acres of potentially cultivable land. Out of this about $1\frac{1}{8}$ acre is *actually* used, by hand or machine cultivation, for the present production of food (and certain non-food crops). Putting this in another way, we can say that it takes the production of a little over 1 acre of cropped land, plus the animal products of open grazing land and plus the products of the forests, to support one 'average' human being. It will be shown later how wide is the actual range in the amount of land required to support one person according to differing standards of living, types of diet, types of farming, and so on; but this world figure is a very useful yardstick. In talking of the potentially cultivable it must be noted that all land with reasonably adequate rainfall and temperature conditions is included, though at present vast areas of such land – the great tropical forests and grasslands, for example – have not yet been tamed and are often virtually uninhabited and entirely undeveloped. The idea that man has yet the technical knowledge to tame these areas is far from the truth: immense research is still needed.

Against these world figures it is interesting to compare – or more often to contrast – some of the nations of the world. If, using the same simple basis, we imagine the land of the United States of America divided equally between all the citizens, the share of each American would be about 11 acres – almost exactly the world average – or 10 acres if Alaska is excluded. Though considerable areas are too arid for permanent settlement and development and there are large tracts of lofty and rugged land, the land capable of sustained production can scarcely be less than 6 acres per head, and improved farmland in crops and grass is actually $3\frac{1}{2}$ acres per head, or three times world average. On any basis of calculation the United States is richly endowed with land.

That great northern neighbour of the United States, Canada, is indeed a giant of untried strength. Every Canadian can lay claim to a share of land totalling 125 acres, of which 22 acres are officially classed as capable of permanent settlement and development and of which 4 acres per head are actually cultivated.

Another 'sleeping giant' is Brazil, with over 30 acres per head, possibly 15 to 20 acres cultivable, but only 1 acre actually used.

Turning to some of the so-called undeveloped countries, the population–land relationship gives a first, admittedly only a first, indication of potential. Take for example Uganda, a well-watered country situated at a healthy elevation astride the African equator. There one finds 10 acres per head, probably 9 acres of them potentially cultivable, only 1 acre at present actually used.

By way of contrast let us look at some of the crowded countries of the world. Although the Republic of India has still 2 acres per head, and Pakistan rather more, there is much arid and mountainous land in both countries, and the potentially cultivable land, if all possible is reclaimed and irrigated, probably does not exceed an acre: land actually used is only about 0·75 acre per head. This, with existing yields, could not support life even at the prevailing low standard of nutrition if it were not for double cropping, and, even so, the bulk of the population is in danger of undernourishment.

Many of the countries of Europe are crowded, indeed so crowded that they are over-populated if they were required to support their existing people on the food produced at home. France is relatively well off with 3 acres per head, about 1·2 acres cultivated; Italy fares badly, by comparison, with 1·5 total acres per head, 0·8 cultivated – hence the strenuous efforts of recent years in land reclamation.

Against these figures those for Britain are particularly instructive. Taking first England, Wales, and Scotland together, land of all sorts – the extensive, almost uninhabited moorland of Scotland and Wales included – amounts to only 1·1 acre per head. For England and Wales the total drops to 0·8 acre. For England and Wales, or for Britain as a whole only 0·55 acre per head is improved land, i.e. farmland in crops and grass. With British systems of farming and British standards of living and range of diet it takes about 1·2 acre of improved farmland to support one person. The record low figure of 1·17 acre was reached under the war effort of 1944–5, the pre-war figure was considerably higher. If 1 acre under British conditions could provide the food for one person it would mean that 55 per cent of total consumption could be home-produced, and this has been named as an official target. If the pressure on land in Britain is thus extreme and has many and varied consequences, it pales into insignificance beside the Japanese position. There the total acreage compares with Britain, 1·1 acre per head, but so much is mountainous that the plains and gentler slopes (less than 1 in 7) capable of cultivation amount to only 0·15 acre per head. Wherever possible the land is double cropped, or treble cropped, but, even allowing for this, each Japanese must exist on the produce of only 0·2 acre. The story of how this is being achieved by concentration on high-calorie foodstuffs (mainly rice and sweet potatoes) and intensive cultivation is one of the staggering stories of present-day agricultural production.

The comparisons given in this chapter are sufficient to indicate the great differences in pressure of population on land resources in the world of today. A very rough rule is to regard all those countries with less than 1 acre of improved farmland as being 'over-populated' in the sense of being unable to support their populations from the home production of food. But this is a very rough rule, to be examined more carefully in a later section.

CHAPTER 4

The Geographical Study of Population

IN the preceding chapter we indicated that one of the greatest of all world problems is the increasing pressure of population on land and land resources, though the pressure at the present day varies greatly from one country to another. It follows logically that there is a great need on the one hand for a factual objective study of population in its many aspects and on the other hand for a similarly objective study of the land, its use or misuse, its actual and potential resources, their exploration and conservation.

Within recent years the study known as demography has made vast strides. The taking of a census has long ceased to be a crude enumeration of people: both the preparation for a census and the analysis of the results involve the use of elaborate and complex techniques. Whilst the statistical analysis of human population is thus well known and well advanced in most countries of the world, much less attention has been paid to the analysis and interpretation of spatial distribution – to the mapping of population and the cartographical representation of population trends.

It is scarcely possible here to consider in detail the numerous ways of representing population on maps, but the principles involved are relatively few and simple.

For census purposes population – classified in various ways according to sex, age, occupation, and so on – is recorded by administrative units. In a country such as Britain, where a decennial census has been taken (except for the war interruption of 1941) from 1801 to 1961, figures are available for the smallest administrative unit – the parish or the town ward. Since the area of each such unit is also known, it is easy to construct crude maps of density – the number of persons per square mile or per acre. The densities may be shown by a range of colours or by varying intensities of shading in black and white. But such crude density maps presume the administrative unit is a homogeneous area with the population evenly distributed over the whole. This is virtually *never* true: a density map on an administrative area basis can never be more than a travesty of the truth. Indeed, by the very nature of its history, the administrative unit is most likely to be a markedly heterogeneous area, whether it be a parish or a county. In the country the original village nucleus probably grew up around a spring or other reliable water supply on fertile cultivable land, leaving the poorer uncultivable, and therefore uninhabited, lands as a barrier between it and the next settlement. In due course the settlements became centres of parishes and their common boundaries were drawn through the poorer no-man's-land between. Such a parish is essentially a heterogeneous area – far from uniform, and with a population far from uniformly distributed.

A more accurate picture of actual population distribution is given by various forms of the dot method. A single dot is allowed to represent a fixed number of people and is placed on the map as nearly as possible where that number live. A concentration of people in a town can be represented by a larger dot or square. Refinements of this method, particularly those developed by Sten de Geer in Sweden, show towns by representations of spheres. There is no reason why a representation of population by the dot method should not be superimposed on a map of population density shown by graded colours – indeed, this is perhaps the best general solution. A partial refinement to this method is to leave white areas known to be uninhabited – for example, large stretches of the moorlands of Scotland – but there is then some doubt whether the remainder should be coloured according to the density over the whole administrative unit or simply that over the part known to be inhabited.

Although in recent years many population maps have been produced in many countries, there is as yet no uniform treatment covering the world on anything but a very small

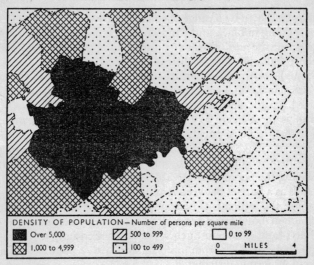

DENSITY OF POPULATION—Number of persons per square mile

■ Over 5,000   ⧄ 500 to 999   ☐ 0 to 99

⊠ 1,000 to 4,999   ⣿ 100 to 499   0   MILES   4

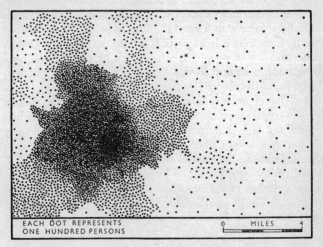

EACH DOT REPRESENTS
ONE HUNDRED PERSONS   0   MILES   4

Fig. 2 (*above and opposite*). Three methods of representing population distribution over a section of the English Midlands around Nottingham

28

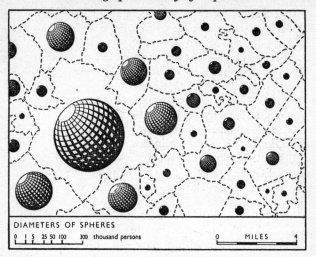

DIAMETERS OF SPHERES

0 1 5 25 50 100   300 thousand persons   0   MILES   4

scale. There is no population map comparable with the
1 : 1,000,000 topographical map which covers the land surface of the world in about 1200 sheets.

When a density distribution map of a considerable area
is prepared using a large number of small administrative
units a definite pattern of distribution begins to appear, and
it is possible to generalize that pattern. Lines (isopleths) are
drawn through points or small areas having the same density, and the resulting isopleth map gives a general idea of
density distribution. But the drawing of such a map involves
a considerable degree of subjective judgement and requires
careful and informed interpretation. It is best made with an
intimate knowledge of the ground.

There is no doubt that population maps correct many
errors difficult to detect from statistical analyses. Two English
counties, for example, may have parishes of roughly the same
size, each with roughly the same number of people, yet in one
case the population may be evenly dispersed in scattered
settlements, in the other grouped in a single nucleated

village. This is easily shown on maps by the dot method. Similarly, two areas in Africa may have the same areas and similar populations. In one case the people are grouped along rivers as the only source of water, in the other carefully avoiding the river banks, either because of liability to flood, or to disease. The distinction is difficult to make statistically, but is at once apparent on a map.

The need for maps of population distribution on a comparable scale and system of representation all over the world, so that the situation in one area can be immediately and directly compared with any other, has led the International Geographical Union to set up an official Commission to work towards this end and to co-ordinate the many separate agencies now working in various areas.

But the essential point about populations is that they are never static. They grow in size, they migrate temporarily or permanently, both within national frontiers and across international boundaries. Since planning consists either in encouraging existing trends where they are believed to be good or countering them when they are considered to be bad, it is obviously extremely important to establish the facts of population growth and change. Much effort has been expended in attempts to show such changes cartographically.

This was seen to be an important matter for British town planners when the Ministry of Town and Country Planning was established in 1943, and the maps prepared by its Maps Office under the control of Dr E. C. Willatts deserve careful study. The general trend of population change in Britain prior to the Second World War was well known, and is exemplified by the period of 1921–31. Although there was an overall increase in population of some 5 per cent – equivalent to 0·5 per cent per annum against a world figure probably between 1·1 and 1·3 – it was known to be greater in the towns than in the country. In fact many rural areas were known definitely to be losing population to such an extent as to have a decreasing total population. The overall change from one census to another can be shown by administrative units by varied shading or colouring. Changes in boundaries of administrative units need to be allowed for, and what is often particularly important is to demonstrate change relative to the country as a whole. If the increase for the country as a whole is 0·5 per cent per annum, an area showing an increase of only 0·2 per cent is in fact decreasing relatively in population. Broadly speaking, all rural areas in Britain show this relative decline, most an actual decline, and the depopulation can be shown to be most severe in areas where physical factors such as inherent poverty of land and difficulty of access are most marked.

Such general maps of changing distribution of population do not separate natural increase – i.e. births and deaths – from population movement or migration. Where facts collected are sufficiently detailed these two aspects of population change can be separated and separately mapped. An overall picture of movement, as well as the same phenomena in a single unit, such as a given town, may be shown by mapping birthplaces of existing population. Whereas statistics may demonstrate this, mapping will often bring out a concentration of migrants in specific areas not revealed statistically. Racial segregation of immigrants is often very clearly marked in American towns. The recent immigration into Britain of coloured people would doubtless show similar concentrations in specific areas.

In Britain the phenomenal growth of certain towns has given rise to a whole set of problems, whilst rural depopulation has set up problems which are nation-wide. In the case of towns it is not as a rule the exact administrative unit – be it urban district, borough, country borough, or city – which is necessarily the important area, so much as the urban area, which may extend by spread of housing into adjoining rural areas or other townships. This fact has brought to the fore the geographical concept of the conurbation. A conurbation – the term introduced by Sir Patrick Geddes – has been variously defined, but is in essence demarcated physically by the existence of houses and other urban buildings. It gives us the very real though ill-defined units, such as Greater

Glasgow, Merseyside, Greater Manchester, Greater Birmingham, the Black Country, and Tyneside. Most marked of all, and defined in many different ways, is Greater London, which has long outgrown the County demarcated to contain it in 1888.

The pattern of urban–industrial Britain has been expanding over the past two centuries – since the Industrial Revolution – swamping, and indeed obliterating the old rural-agricultural pattern, with its farms, hamlets, villages, and market towns, which had steadily evolved over the previous 2,000 years or more. One of the great questions of the present day is whether the rural parish and the truly rural village are still viable units. To enable precise studies to be

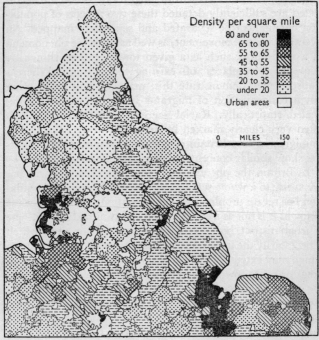

Density per square mile

80 and over
65 to 80
55 to 65
45 to 55
35 to 45
20 to 35
under 20
Urban areas

0   MILES   150

Fig. 3. Density of rural population over parts of England and Wales

made of this special and pressing problem I suggested the division of the rural population into (*a*) primary rural – those people and their dependants, mainly farmers and farm workers, dependent directly on the land for their living; (*b*) secondary rural – those people with their dependants existing to provide essential services for the primary rural; and (*c*) adventitious – those people who live in the country by choice, including many retired people. There are some parts of Britain which may be very fertile agriculturally – such as parts of the Fens – but which do not attract an adventitious population. Dr S. W. E. Vince has shown that in those areas almost exactly two-thirds of the people are primary rural, one-third secondary rural. Owing to the increased efficiency of farming and the substitution of much mechanization for hand labour, as well as the shift of such servicing as farm-implement repairs to the towns, the difficulty is to find enough people to maintain village life – to support the church, chapel, cricket, and football teams, and even to patronize the village 'pub', and especially to provide enough children to keep the village school going. It was an early tenet of planning in the nineteen-forties that new building in the country should be restricted to the needs of agriculture – farmers and farm workers – so as to prevent the alienation of productive farmland, but this was reversed when it was found that an adventitious population is essential to maintain the ordinary village services.

The problem of the structure of the rural population, just mentioned, raises the question of the changing age structure of population. Where the birth rate is high, a large percentage of the total population is naturally found in the lower age groups. Contrasts are clearly apparent when the figures are shown in the diagrammatic form known as fir-tree diagrams.

In the age composition of populations the countries of the world fall very roughly into four groups:

1. The old-settled crowded countries (such as most of the countries of Europe) where the pressure of population

on land is very severe. The birth rate is low – hence a small proportion in the lower age groups – but medical services are highly developed, and most people live to a good age and there is a high proportion in the higher age groups. The 12 per cent of the people of Britain over sixty-five are mainly retired and constitute something of a burden on the community as a whole.

II. The old-settled crowded countries (such as India and China) where birth control is not yet general and where medical services are not yet fully developed and expectation of life at birth remains comparatively low. These show a high proportion of the population in the lower age groups, a small proportion in the highest.

III. The newer-settled countries, especially the Roman Catholic countries of Latin America, where birth control is not generally practised and where the birth rate, at 4·0 or more per cent per annum, is the highest in the world, but where medical services are not yet fully organized to combat disease and where consequently the proportion of the population in the higher age groups is small.

IV. The newer-settled countries where pressure of population on resources is scarcely as yet a pressing problem and where an expanding economy encourages an expanding family. At the same time 'death control' is well advanced and there is a good expectation of life. The outstanding examples are the United States and Canada: Australia and New Zealand show similar features.

It will be clear that the countries of the world offer many contrasts to Britain in the changing character of population. If one accepts the world population increase to be 1·8 per cent per annum, it is instructive to show on a map of the world those countries where the increase is in excess of this average. Contrary to popular belief, it is not in the monsoon countries of south-east Asia, already crowded, or in Mediterranean Europe, also very crowded, but in the wide open spaces of the Americas. The trend is, of course, accentuated by the dominant migration into these areas, and this helps to explain the fact that the English-speaking white races are increasing four times as rapidly as the population of the world as a whole. After centuries of little growth, the population of Africa is probably increasing rapidly.

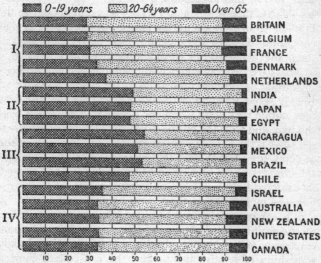

Fig. 4. The age-composition of the population in some contrasted countries

An aspect of population growth which is often overlooked is that the increase in number of families, each requiring a home, is not the same as the total population increase. If the average family consists of parents and three children, a family of five in all, twenty units of accommodation will be needed for every 100 total population. But if the average family is, as in Britain, only 3·2, then thirty-one units will be needed per 100 of population. The demand on land for houses is increased accordingly. In Britain the demand for houses has thus grown more than the increase in population would at first suggest.

The family structure has of course numerous other effects. After the artificial conditions of the Second World War there was something of a rush to re-establish normal family life – to make up, as it were, for lost time – and the number of births in 1947 was far in excess of the normal or average of any recent ten-year period. In due course the children born in this and succeeding years have come to primary school age, then to secondary school age, and appear as the familiar 'bulge' straining the existing resources for higher education. Though the demand must be satisfied at each stage, the 'bulge' is to a considerable extent temporary.

Not so the general ageing of the population, with an ever-increasing percentage appearing in the higher age groups. If sixty is looked upon as the normal retiring age, the time may not be far distant when one person in every five is over this age, and so living on the productive labour of others. If sixty-five is the normal retiring age, some 12 per cent, or one in eight, are already over that age. It is small wonder that the Universities of Oxford and Cambridge as early as 1956 saw the red light and fixed sixty-seven as the retiring age – followed by London in 1957.

What may be called the burden of the ageing population on the nation as a whole is naturally increased as additional consideration is given to 'old-age pensioners' – already something of a misnomer – and the consequent burden through taxation on the productive working-age group is one of the factors leading to the emigration overseas of the latter. If whole families – grandfather and grandmother together with the breadwinner, his wife, and children – emigrate all may be well, but the selective emigration of those in the middle-age groups leaving over-age dependants in Britain increases the burden on those who remain.

In 1962 a new trend, already apparent in the United States, was observed in Britain. There was a marked rise in the birth rate. With increased prosperity there is a definite tendency for people to marry earlier and have larger families.

CHAPTER 5

The Land

MANY town and country planners would undoubtedly be very much happier if they could regard the land as a blank sheet of paper on which they could develop their ideas for the future. Actually this is very far from being the case, and the land already presents an extremely complex pattern of different types of use. In one of the older settled countries of Europe, for instance Great Britain, this complex land-use pattern is the result of many hundreds, indeed thousands, of years of settlement. It represents the interaction of the physical factors, the historical factors, the social factors, and the economic factors. In one of the newer settled countries of the world, such as the United States, it is true that the land-use pattern has not nearly such a deep meaning as it has in western Europe. It might be thought that in some of the sparsely populated areas of the world, such as the grasslands of Africa or of South America, Nature was responsible almost entirely for the existing use or non-use of land. The more, however, the matter is studied, the more it is realized that man's interference with Nature is apparent even in these remoter areas. It would seem obvious that one of the first things which must be done before there can be any planning for the future is to record the present position, and to seek to understand the reason for that present position: why some land has been settled and developed and is highly productive, while other parts of the land in any country have remained virtually unpopulated and virtually untouched by the hand of man or by his grazing animals. Indeed, we can go so far as to say that there ought really to be three stages in this work of using land to the best possible advantage.

There ought first to be the stage of survey, the recording of the present position; secondly, the stage of analysis (discussed in the next chapter), seeking to understand the reasons for that position and of seeing what are the existing trends in development; and then, thirdly, the actual planning for the future (discussed in Chapter 7), which must take the present and the present trends into full consideration. Unfortunately this concept of land-use planning is far from being universally accepted. There is an idea that surely there must be a short cut, that one can ignore the past, one can ignore the present, and go straight on to say what should be done for the future. Speaking personally, I regard this as an extremely dangerous point of view, and consider that one of the great essentials should be a survey – a detailed objective study – of the present use of the land.

When in October 1930 I organized the Land Utilisation Survey of Britain it was with the idea of finding out exactly what use was then being made of every acre of England, Wales, and Scotland. One of the most important aspects of the education of young people is to teach them to observe carefully and accurately, and so very much of our Survey was carried out in the nineteen-thirties as a voluntary exercise from the schools and colleges of Britain. The work was done entirely on the Ordnance Survey maps on the scale of 6 inches to 1 mile. These are published to cover the whole of the country, and the quarter-sheets in which they are normally issued represent 3 miles from east to west, and 2 miles from north to south. Thus to survey one quarter-sheet means covering an area of 6 square miles or 3,840 acres.* All those who are familiar with the 6-inch maps will know that they show every field and every building, and that they are true to scale. It was therefore the task of the young surveyors to look at every field, and to record quite simply on the map the use actually being made of it at the time according to a simple scheme of classification which was given to them. The work was organized on a county basis, with a county organizer for every one of the adminis-

* Since the work of the Land Utilisation Survey a new series of 6-inch maps of different size is being issued.

trative counties of England, Wales, and Scotland. Very often the local administrator was the Director of Education, and it is estimated that something like a quarter of a million schoolchildren took part in the work. Many teachers organized it most skilfully; they introduced an element of competition among the children, seeing who could be the most accurate observers, recording the facts properly, seeing who could produce the best maps, the most neatly executed, and the most fully documented. In many cases tracings of the 6-inch maps were handed out to individual children and their results were compared. There were of course parts of the country where survey by the schools was not possible, and parties of University students and graduates were encouraged to cover these. To cut short the long story, the bulk of the country was actually surveyed, the land use recorded, in the years 1931, 1932, and 1933. There remained some small parts which had to be completed later, but the whole was virtually finished before the outbreak of war in 1939, and before the beginning of the plough-up campaign which made such an enormous difference to land use in this country.

The Land Utilisation Survey of Britain for the nineteen-thirties was often compared with the Domesday Survey. It had no ulterior motive, which the Domesday Survey had in the matter of taxation, and its object was simply to record the factual position. It took place at a time when agriculture in Britain was at one of its lowest ebbs for many a long year, and so the picture is that of British agriculture at its nadir. One may rightly ask: Was the work of these young and so largely untrained volunteer surveyors sufficiently accurate to be of value? The answer quite simply is: Yes. It is of course remarkable how familiar are those who are born and bred in the country with the varied farm crops; they are accustomed also to finding their way about the country, and once they are taught to read a detailed map with accuracy they have no difficulty in recording the facts on the maps. There is no doubt, too, that their parents took a very lively interest in this work and much help was gained from them.

When one remembers that the surveyor of one quarter sheet of the 6-inch map did not know who was responsible for those sheets which lay on the four sides, it will be realized that a very severe statistical check was possible all along the margins of each sheet. Naturally the work was checked, but it was only quite rarely that a sheet had to be thrown out for obvious inaccuracies. They were checked by many seniors, including myself, who did traverses by road and by footpath across sheets to test their accuracy. So I have little fear on this important score. Let me say at once that the task was by no means a small one, in that it requires something like 15,000 separate sheets to cover the whole of Great Britain. When the sheets were received from the counties, the work of editing and reduction to the 1-inch scale began, and the first map to be published was actually issued on 1 January 1933. From that time onwards the work progressed steadily, and the published record takes the form of fully coloured maps on the scale of 1 inch to 1 mile. In due course these were issued for the whole of England and Wales and for all the more populous parts of Scotland. There are, of course, in the Highlands of Scotland many areas very sparsely populated where the expense of issuing the sheets was not felt to be fully justified, but the manuscript 1-inch sheets are preserved and available for study in the library of the Royal Geographical Society. In addition a map of the whole of Britain, which had to be generalized, on the scale of roughly 10 miles to 1 inch, or 1 : 625,000, was in due course issued in the National Planning Series, printed by the Ordnance Survey and published by the Ministry, which was then the Ministry of Town and Country Planning.

The classification of land use which was used was the result of a number of pioneer experiments in different parts of the country, and we will reproduce here the instructions which were given in the leaflet to surveyors as far as the classification of land use is concerned.

NOTES ON THE CLASSIFICATION

1. Forests and woodland are usually marked on the 6-inch maps, but all the areas must be checked. Care must be taken to include the newly planted areas. When this has been done the woodland must be classified as follows:

A High Forest, big trees, sufficiently close for their crowns to touch; also state whether the trees are Coniferous, Deciduous, Mixed.

B Coppice, or coppice with standards, woodland that is cut over every few years, for fencing, posts, etc.

C Scrub, any small bushes or trees unfit for cutting.

D A Forest, cut down and not replanted. This requires a note stating its present character.

A note should also be made against any forest or woodland which is not intended to supply timber, but is ornamental, for screening houses and gardens, etc.

In practice it has been found that the simplest way of dealing with forest or woodland on the field map is as follows: Mark each piece of forest with the letter F; then distinguish its character according to the above classification as FA, FB, FC, FD. Then distinguish character of trees by small symbols c, d, m. Dominant trees may be named.

2. Meadowland and Permanent Grass (M). Care must be taken not to include rotation grass (grass grown in rotation with crops) under this classification.

3. Arable or tilled land includes rotation grass and fallow land (A). Rotation grass is often indicated by a large proportion of clover. At the present time, when much land which was recently arable is being converted to permanent grassland, its appearance, showing evidence of recent cultivation, gives rise to doubt as to whether it is Arable or Meadow. In such cases, information should be obtained from the farmer. A point, easily recorded, which may well be added to the map is the crop actually being grown at the

date of the Survey. Market Gardens are arable, being merely a special form of agriculture, and should accordingly be marked A. Where it is quite clear that they are market gardens, they should be marked A (M.G.).

4. Heathland, Moorland, Commons, and Rough Hill Pasture (H). This type of land is usually already distinguished on the 6-inch maps. Swamps and marshes are often used as rough pasture, and should be included here. It is advisable to make a special note against any land where there is any doubt, saying what use is made of it.

5. Gardens, Allotments, Orchards, Nurseries, etc. Houses with gardens sufficiently large to grow a few vegetables or even flowers should be marked G (garden) since the area is productive. Backyards and other areas agriculturally unproductive should, however, be marked W. Allotments are merely gardens at a distance from the house. Orchards are usually already distinguished on the maps (but should, of course, be checked). They must be marked O. In some orchards, in addition to the fruit trees, the ground is used for grazing or for agriculture. In such cases they should be marked O (M) when used for fruit and pasture, or O (A) when used for fruit and ground crops.

6. Unproductive Land (W). This includes buildings, yards, mines, cemeteries, and waste land, i.e. all ground of which the soil is not productively used. It is advisable to make a special note stating the character of all considerable areas marked (W).

OTHER POINTS

Parks should be classified according to the use of the land, e.g. pasture, woodland, gardens, etc. Public parks are large gardens used by the public, and should be marked G.

Golf courses can sometimes be used for grazing, and then are permanent grassland (M). Others are heathland and moorland (H). Mark them also with the words 'Golf Course'.

Sports Grounds are usually grassland, but where devoted

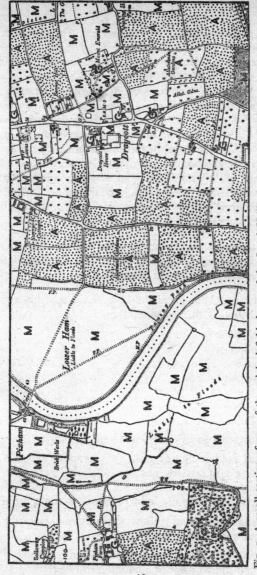

Fig. 5. A small section of one of the original field sheets of the Land Utilisation Survey of Britain showing categories of land use

entirely to sports, they should be specially distinguished, e.g. M (Sports).

Poultry Farms usually occur on meadowland. A special note should be made against them.

New Buildings, Roads, etc., made since the map was printed should be sketched in as far as possible. In the case of a new building estate it is not necessary to mark in every house, but the general plan of the roads and lines of houses should be indicated, and in the case of undeveloped estates the approximate boundaries should be ascertained and a note made of the estates. When a whole area is marked off as 'Building Estate' a note should be added as to whether it is undeveloped (lying waste); partly developed (scattered dwellings), or more fully developed.

A certain amount of simplification had to take place for the production of the 1-inch maps, and the legend for a typical 1-inch map is given below.

Forests and Woodland (dark green, superimposed on Ordnance Survey symbol):

Deciduous
Coniferous
Mixed
New plantations

Arable Land (brown):

Including fallow, rotation grass, and market gardens

Meadowland and Permanent Grass (light green):

Land available for grazing, such as sports grounds and some golf courses, has been included here. The distinction between low-lying meadows and ordinary pasture can be made by reference to the contours

Heath and Moorland (yellow, superimposed on Ordnance Survey symbol):

Heath, moorland, commons, and rough pasture
Rough marsh pasture, including saltings

Areas formerly improved but which have been allowed
to revert to rough pasture or heathland are included

Houses with gardens sufficiently large to be productive
of fruit, vegetables, flowers, etc. (purple)

Orchards (purple superimposed on Ordnance Survey
symbol, or purple ruling)

New housing areas, nurseries, allotments, and new
orchards (solid purple)

Land Agriculturally Unproductive (red):

Land so closely covered with houses and other buildings or industrial work as to be agriculturally unproductive

Yards, cemeteries, pits, quarries, tip heaps, new industrial works, etc.

What, we may now ask, does such a survey of land use
actually show? In the first place, it does not matter what
sheet one examines, one is struck by the extremely complex
pattern which is presented by the use or non-use of land in
this country. In the second place, if one takes, for example,
a sheet from the drier east of England, with the bulk of the
land cultivated and under corn crops, and contrasts it with
an area from the west – let us say the mountains of Wales or
of Scotland – one has emphasized the point which has already been made, of the extreme difference between the
conditions in one part of our small country and those in another. In other words, the differences in the physical conditions, notably relief, soil, and rainfall, produce land-use patterns of very different types in the two areas. Much information can be obtained by just studying the maps, but
one soon finds, in attempting to reach a reasonable explanation for the distribution, let us say, of ploughed land,
that one is puzzled by what appear to be anomalies. One
asks oneself: Is it a question of soil, is it a question of ownership, or are there some other subtle factors which are not
apparent just from the reading of the map? It was in order
to help the interpretation that the Land Utilisation Survey

of Britain undertook the publication of a series of explanatory memoirs, one for each county. Eventually the ninety-two parts were issued, and form a mine of information, in each case attempting to explain what was then the present position.

The importance of understanding the present land-use pattern shown by the different countries of the world has come in recent years to be more and more readily appreciated. With the increasing pressure of population on land comes the need for careful planning of land resources in all countries of the world. It is obviously more urgent in those countries which are very densely populated than it is in those countries where the population is still sparse or widely scattered, but the need exists everywhere. It was not surprising, therefore, that at the Congress called by the International Geographical Union in Lisbon at Easter, 1949, a project was brought forward by Professor Samuel Van Valkenburg, the Head of the Graduate School of Geography at Clark University, Worcester, Massachusetts, to form a commission which would look into the question of drawing up what he called a Land Use Inventory for all countries in the world. The idea was supported by the United Nations Educational, Scientific, and Cultural Organization UNESCO), which gave an initial grant to enable a small commission of five persons to get together and thrash out proposals. The commission met at Worcester, Massachusetts, in the following year, and it drew up its schemes for a World Land-use Survey.

It so happened that after discussing many possible classifications of land, the one which was finally regarded as applicable to all parts of the world is in fact very closely related to the scheme which was used by the British Land Utilisation Survey. The proposals for classification of land are given below:

1. Settlements and associated non-agricultural lands (dark and light red)
2. Horticulture (deep purple)

3. Tree and other perennial crops (light purple)
4. Cropland:
    A Continual and rotation cropping (dark brown)
    B Land rotation (light brown)
5. Improved permanent pasture (managed or enclosed) (light green)
6. Unimproved grazing land:
    A Used (orange)
    B Not used (yellow)
7. Woodlands:
    A Dense (dark green)
    B Open (medium green)
    C Scrub (olive green)
    D Swamp forests (blue green)
    E Cut over or burnt over forest areas (green stipple)
    F Forest with subsidiary cultivation (green with brown dots)
8. Swamps and marshes (fresh- and salt-water, non-forested) (blue)
9. Unproductive land (grey).

It is obviously quite impossible for a single organization to carry out a detailed land-use survey of the whole world, and the World Land Use Survey which was set up as a result of the Commission's activities had as its twin aims: first, the testing out of methods of work, particularly in testing out the usefulness of air photographs, and secondly, the stimulation of work all over the world along lines which would enable surveys carried out nationally to be readily comparable one with the other. It is obviously not of very great use if the survey in one country is on a different basis from that in another; one cannot compare the results, and mutual aid is rendered impossible. The Commission rendered reports on its work to the Washington Congress in 1952, the Rio Congress in 1956, and Stockholm in 1960; and it was possible to record land-use surveys in progress in very many countries of the world, particularly in those forward-looking countries which recognize the vital significance of planning scientifically and effectively their future use of land. Eastern Pakistan, for example, had commissioned an aerial survey of the great area of the Indus Basin, upon which the future of that country must so clearly depend for the further production of foodstuffs for home use and for export. To take another large example, the Canadian Government arranged for an aerial survey of the vast tracts of forest-land which are so difficult to study from the ground, and land-use maps have been made of those areas for future use.

Some of the pioneer studies carried out by the London headquarters of the World Land Use Survey were on areas in Africa, notably in Tanganyika and Nyasaland, where the huge extent of bush, very sparsely inhabited, naturally gives the idea of vast tracts of country varying very little from one part to another. Indeed, the World Land Use Survey recommended survey and publication on the scale of 1 : 1,000,000, which is approximately 16 miles to 1 inch. It was found in practice, however, that the air photographs showed a most remarkably complex character of vegetation and land-use in those areas. There were little patches of cultivation here and there, and soon the question arose why the inhabitants had chosen those particular areas for their use. The idea that conditions are more or less the same over vast tracts was undoubtedly mainly responsible for the gigantic failure of the East African Groundnut Scheme, carried out without such a survey as now recommended, carried out without a pilot experiment, and so resulting in the enormous loss of money borne almost entirely by the British taxpayer. Undoubtedly this would have been obviated had a land-use survey of the type which is now being recommended been carried out in the area.

Using air photographs, the Survey, with the help of Mr R. R. Rawson and Mr K. R. Sealy of the London School of Economics, has recently prepared and published a map of the whole of Cyprus.

Perhaps no country has taken up the work more enthusiastically than Japan. The crucial problem there is how to support a huge population of some 90 million on the small

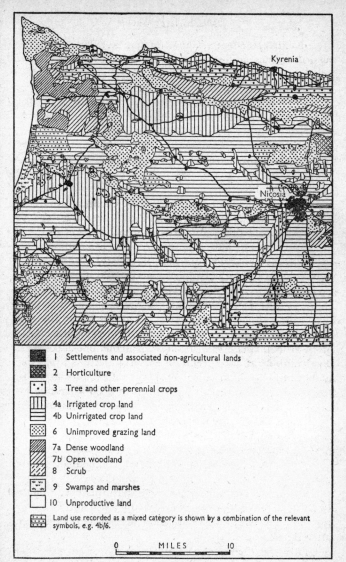

▓	1 Settlements and associated non-agricultural lands
▒	2 Horticulture
∴	3 Tree and other perennial crops
‖‖‖	4a Irrigated crop land
≡	4b Unirrigated crop land
░	6 Unimproved grazing land
▨	7a Dense woodland
╱╱	7b Open woodland
╱╱╱	8 Scrub
⟡	9 Swamps and marshes
☐	10 Unproductive land
	Land use recorded as a mixed category is shown by a combination of the relevant symbols, e.g. 4b/6.

```
0          MILES          10
```

Fig. 6. Portion of the land-use map of Cyprus showing the categories of existing land use recommended by the World Land Use Survey

area of cultivable land, even when intensively used. It is not surprising that land-use survey has been given the highest priority.

As we shall see, however, in a later chapter, the recording of the existing use and non-use of land is one thing, but the question of land classification – that is to say, the attempt to measure the inherent qualities of land – is quite a different matter.

Again, too, there are different methods of expressing land use, and different uses of colours. It should be mentioned here that some very remarkable maps have been produced under the guidance of Professor Henri Gaussen of parts of France, French North Africa, and elsewhere. He has the concept not only of mapping existing use, but using a scheme of colours which shall express the physical conditions responsible for the present position. In general, he aims to use dark colours where the factors concerned – it may be aridity or excessive moisture – are far from the normal, and to express the normal by very pale colours, or none at all. Thus the fertile cultivated areas stand out in his maps, through the absence of colour, but have on them signs indicating crops grown. It is a very ingenious scheme, but of course it does combine an interpretation – that is to say, a subjective judgement – with an objective survey and the recording of facts, whereas the British proposal is to keep these two aspects quite separate, to deal only with the recording of facts on the initial land-use maps.

Although we have referred in this chapter to land use, it should be noted that the non-use of land is also recorded, and in those areas which are sparsely populated, or not populated at all by human beings, the division of land in detail is really one of natural or semi-natural vegetation, so that one does combine what is virtually a vegetation survey in such areas with a survey of those areas which have been altered or occupied by man.

Under the direction of Miss Alice Coleman of King's College, London, a second land-use survey of England and Wales, more elaborate than the first, is now in progress.

CHAPTER 6

The Interpretation of the Population and Land-use Patterns

IN the densely populated countries of the Old World, the complex pattern of population distribution and present land use is the result of centuries, indeed millennia, of human settlement and development. Little, if any, remains of the 'natural' vegetation cover; all has been subject to the varying impact of man's activities, especially through the domestic animals he has tamed or the wild animals he has tolerated. When mapping land use in one of the older countries the pattern is often so fine, so intricate, that it can only be shown on such large-scale maps as 1 : 10,000 (the British series is on the scale of 6 inches to the mile, or 1 : 10,560). Even then such a distinctive habitat for wild flowers as a hedgerow can only be indicated approximately. The complex, intricate pattern of land use or non-use is the result of the action and interaction of many factors: some physical, such as elevation, slope, drainage, soil, rainfall, and temperature; others historical, such as ownership and tenure; others more purely economic, such as working costs and agricultural prices. In the older settled countries the period of experiment – of determining appropriate land use by trial and error – is long past and the patterns of land use are far more stable than in newer areas.

But whatever the reason for the present complex pattern, it is from this and upon this that any planning for the future must start. Our land is not a blank sheet of paper to be planned *de novo*.

In the newer countries of the world, where settlement, at least in any intensive form, is only a few generations old, the position may be different. The present land-use pattern is the result of a few decades of trial and error: actual use may be far from suggesting potential use. It is not surprising that some investigators, especially those trained in the wide-open spaces of the poor misused land of the United States, like to concentrate on land potential and to ignore present use.

When we turn to the study of the vast stretches of such areas as tropical Africa and South America, there are thus two approaches which tend to be very different. One is to map and study intensively the present position, trying to determine why present settlement and cultivation are where they are, and so to evaluate the potent factors. The other is to concentrate on the major factors, such as relief, water supply, and especially soil, and so to suggest potential use, ignoring the present position. It is sometimes argued that the problems are so urgent that there is not time to carry out either type of survey. Development schemes are put into operation without either the present position being fully known or the potential properly assessed. It was this which led to the colossal waste of money – about £35 million – on the East African Groundnut Scheme. This is by no means an isolated example of an abortive project based on a hasty assessment of potential. In the case of the East African scheme it has since been realized that the few productive patches in the area had long been discovered and used by the 'ignorant' (often very wise) African cultivators.

I would plead therefore for the two basic maps, the population map and the land-use map, to be regarded as fundamental needs. They both show facts of distribution.

The next stage is the interpretation – seeking to know and understand the factors which have led to the present position. Both the population pattern and the land-use pattern may be so complex that it is helpful first to dissect them. In the case of population, for example, an analysis where possible by occupation serves to separate a scattered agricultural community from concentrations due to exploitation of minerals.

Based therefore on the cartographical interpretation or the mapping of population, one may visualize a number of maps which express the facts of distribution. There is first the map which has been mentioned above of total population showing its distribution. This leaves no doubt that there are some areas where population is concentrated, some areas where population is sparse or absent. It is a factual picture of the position. Then there may be other maps, for example the one in which one separates the urban from the rural population, which will stress the concentration of urban population in its certain centres. Then the various maps showing the population by occupation – again stressing that certain types of occupation are concentrated in certain areas. Similarly, one can extend this picture and have maps which show population migration, or population increment or decrease. This brings the time factor into consideration and shows where movement is taking place. Britain is fortunate in that the essential data for the construction of such maps are usually available. Unfortunately this is not true of the underdeveloped countries of the world: precisely in areas where most needed information is lacking and difficult to collect.

All the maps suggested are essentially factual, and the next stage in the geographical analysis is to attempt the interpretation. But before dealing with the interpretation of the population maps, let us look also at the maps concerned with the use of land.

A useful analysis of the use or non-use of land is to separate the main categories and to show them separately. If, for example, the moorland or rough grazing of Britain is shown separately (as in Fig. 7), its concentration on the upland parts of Highland Britain and its spread to lower ground in the wet north-west are at once apparent, and the various smaller areas stand out clearly.

Similarly, if the ploughed lands of the country are shown separately one sees clearly the concentration over the lowlands of the drier east. Fig. 8 refers to the pre-war position, before the plough-up campaign of the nineteen-forties altered the picture in the grassy Midlands, but the distribution is so striking as to demand an explanation.

In the attempt to interpret the land-use pattern of Britain

Fig. 7. The moorlands or rough grazing of Britain

revealed by the Land Utilisation Survey not only were these
two categories – moorland and arable – taken off and shown
separately, but also the permanent grassland, and the forest

Fig. 8. The arable land of England and Wales

and woodland. These four categories naturally covered the greater part of the country; each revealed a quite distinctive pattern. Covering smaller areas were other categories of land, for example, orchards – a very discontinuous distribution in Britain. Particularly interesting was the distribution of houses with gardens – where housing had been constructed with sufficiently open density to afford gardens large enough to be productive of fruit and vegetables. Then another map, the red of the original, is land closely built over. The last two together of course represent the main concentrations of population as they are shown by the actual area which is occupied by the dwellings of the people and by the buildings they have constructed in connexion with their daily life. By this cartographical analysis we get a series of maps again simply illustrating the factual position. As in the case of population, we can add to this the question of change by mapping similarly, where information is available, the distribution as it has been in various past times. But let us see how the geographer proceeds to an analysis of what he finds in such maps by looking now at the factors which have led to the present position in Britain.

In a similar way the influencing factors can be isolated, and the relevant facts with regard to them can be mapped. One finds oneself then comparing a succession of maps. It is often difficult to do this with a series side by side, and hence a very common device is to use a series of transparencies, where certain facts can be printed on transparent paper and two or more maps placed one above the other. It is often then possible at least to suggest that certain factors are responsible for the observed distribution of population or land use.

We may divide the relevant factors into three rather rough groups. There are first the physical factors; second the historical factors; and third the socio-economic factors. Some sociologists and economists will claim that all factors concerned come within their sphere, and so 'socio-economic' is used perhaps in a rather narrow sense. The geographer with the emphasis on the *ge*, on the earth, will naturally start with the more obvious of the physical factors. Undoubtedly the most obvious is the relief of the land: the orographic factor. It is quite unnecessary to point out that high plateaux and mountains become devoid of population through sheer elevation, and one can see this correlation in Britain when one maps for example the land over 600 or 800 or 1,000 feet. There is little cultivation above 1,000 feet in the south of England, very little over 600 or 800 feet as one goes northwards. We can of course go so far as to say that certain areas of the world can be eliminated as being incapable of supporting any permanent settlement based on agricultural production on any land above a certain elevation. The elevation naturally varies from one part of the world to another. In Britain it may be as high as 1,250 or even 1,500 feet in some parts, but normally 1,000 feet or less. Apart from elevation there is another important factor, and that is the relief of the land in the minor sense; to what extent it may or may not be broken up by steep slopes. Various methods have been devised for illustrating this question of prevalence of steep slopes. One simple yet quite effective method is to divide the country into squares of a given size and to show the highest and the lowest points in each square as an indication of the amount of dissection and consequently the dominant steepness of slope. This brings out the unsuitability of even some low ground for intensive cultivation because of the absence of flat areas. In other cases there may be large tracts, as in the great prairies of the United States and Canada, where the land, despite its elevation, is level or gently undulating, and therefore capable of settlement and of agricultural development.

Another important series of factors which greatly influence the distribution of population, and often the use of the land, are those which are associated with its geological structure. Not unnaturally one thinks in terms of the distribution of useful minerals and the correlation which that gives with certain pockets of population which would not otherwise be present. Minerals attract population to areas which would certainly not be occupied by people engaged in farming or forestry alone. The most obvious correlation of this sort is of course between the coalfields of Britain and the industrial areas which grew up with the Industrial Revolution, when the main concentrations of population shifted quite definitely from the areas of most fertile and productive agricultural land to those where the new source of power, coal, was obtained. But there are other correlations with geological maps which are perhaps more subtle. There can be no doubt whatsoever, when one puts side by side the map showing the principal ploughed lands of England and Wales and a geological map, that certain geological formations, or more strictly the soils derived from them, favour arable cultivation, whereas others, the heavy clays, favour the use of the land in permanent grass. In much the same way certain of the geological formations which yield very light, sandy soils are associated with low-land heaths. We cannot work out the exact correlations we should like in Britain because of the absence of a complete series of drift maps, and after all it is the drift, the superficial deposits so widely distributed in Britain, which most directly influence the development of soil, and so the type of farming.

There can be no doubt of the enormous importance of climate in this country. The rainfall map, with the very heavy rainfall areas on the hillier lands in the west, the belt of moderate rainfall in the Midlands, where the total per year is between 30 and 60 inches, and the rather more limited areas in the east of the country, where the total rainfall drops below 30 inches, shows at once the great influence which the amount of rainfall has on farming occupations. It is only in the drier east of England that the ripening of cereal crops and arable farming are really favoured. Elsewhere our climate is much more suitable for the growth of grass, fodder crops, the grass either permanent or grown in rotation or long ley. We are perhaps apt to forget the significance of other climatic factors. In the summer the south of this country is considerably warmer than the north. Going northward we reach the stage when there is really an inadequate total amount of summer warmth for the ripening of certain crops, though this may be partly offset by the greater length of summer daylight. We may say that in England as a whole, except in certain favoured localities, we are in this regard beyond the limit for the economic cultivation of maize. Similarly we reach the economic limit of cultivation of wheat within the British Isles, whereas barley can be, provided it is not too damp, extensively cultivated right away to the north. Perhaps even more interesting is the field, still not properly explored, of the influence of micro-climatic conditions, or variations locally in climate, on the cultivation of the land. In fact the whole question of the influence of minor climatic changes is a fundamental one. We talk quite commonly in ordinary speech of the advantages of being on the sunny side of the street, we know the advantages of a southern aspect, and of a house which catches the sun; although all these points are familiar, they are not taken into consideration nearly as much as they should be in planning the use of the land.

It is only recently, for example, that we have thought in terms of the existence of frost pockets as affecting the location of our new housing estates. It would be possible to point to some of the housing estates which have been built even in these post-war years which have been located in some of the worst possible climatic situations in the areas concerned, where a down-draught of cold, heavy air is liable to accumulate and cause the maintenance of mist and fog for a longer period than anywhere else. This is a matter which very much needs the attention of our planners, especially those who are concerned in town planning. We of course have been brought face to face with the problem in the location of some of our airports, where the existence of tracts foggier than others has ruled out certain otherwise suitable locations. On the other hand, there are places which have high sunshine records which use these to persuade visitors that these are the areas where they can find the right conditions which they seek for their summer holidays. Or, similarly, there are those sunnier places which attract retired people who prefer the advantages of Ventnor or Bournemouth, whereas their working lives may have been spent in the heart of Manchester.

Local climatic differences have also a profound effect on rural land use. All gardeners are familiar with the importance of micro-climate in a garden: what can be grown in a sunny border is quite different from what will flourish on a north-facing wall. The farmer knows that each type of soil not only has its own climate – heavy clay soils, because of their high water content, heat up slowly in spring and are cold and late – but the soil influences the micro-climate of the air with which it is in contact. Local winds, such as those sweeping down a funnel-like valley, are factors to be reckoned with, and many parts of Britain benefit from windbreaks of trees planted to counteract such effects. Yet those same windbreaks in other circumstances may hold up the flow of cold, heavy air in winter and give rise to frost pockets.

The historical factors which have affected the land-use pattern are frequently more difficult to isolate. Yet there are many important cases. For example, the continued existence of such areas as Epping Forest, the New Forest, and the Forest of Dean is in part a result of poverty of soil. More important, they are the present-day remnants of those Royal Forests which were deliberately laid out hundreds of years ago for the enjoyment of the King and his nobles. Similarly, many a valued open space today is the common or waste land which was left by the Lord of the Manor for the pasturing of animals by his commoners. Frequently it was land which was not attractive for cultivation which was left in this way; but that is not always the case. In this day few people can afford still to live in the stately homes of England in the midst of their own private and extensive parkland. Yet in so many cases those very parklands have preserved from destruction and building the open spaces we need so badly in or near our towns. This again is the historical accident of ownership. Many other cases might be quoted of how the historical factor has influenced present-day use of land. The field pattern of small, irregularly shaped fields so characteristic of most of lowland Britain marks the sometimes rather hurried carrying out of enclosure awards by planting of quickset hedges; once established, it is difficult to change.

Turning to the third group of factors, the socio-economic, perhaps we can include there the question of access. Looking at the railway and road networks, there are parts of the country not easily reached by either rail or main road. It is little use the farmer there producing perishable commodities intended for immediate consumption. In recent years the growth of motor transport has, however, made possible the extension of milk production in the remotest valleys of Wales, where previously any excess of milk had to be turned by the farmer into farm-house butter or cheese. Another interesting case may be quoted from the south-east of England, in Kent, where the development of motor transport made possible the extension of fruit cultivation in the belt to the immediate east of Canterbury, not served by railway. Until the development of direct road transport this area could not send its fruit in a sufficiently fresh condition for the London market. There are still, however, many remote parts of Britain where the difficulty of access remains an important factor. Probably much more use could be made of some of the fine, light, sandy lands – the machar – of the western coasts of Scotland, especially on some of the islands, if only those islands were not islands, but were connected with the mainland. It has been shown by recent investigation by our Ministry of Agriculture, Fisheries, and Food that improvement of farm access would probably make a great deal of difference to the use of land, for example in those parts of Northumberland bordering on the Cheviots. There the land is intrinsically good, but roads are few and poor.

The traditional way of life is something, too, which affects the use of land. There are parts of this country where the tradition is the family farm. Units are small, there is no tradition of farm labour, and therefore the size of the holding and the whole operation of farming is limited by the fact that all the work must be done by the farmer and his family. By way of contrast, it may be said that much of the fruit and vegetable production in the Vale of Evesham and elsewhere is only possible because of labour which is available at the time of the fruit or potato harvests from the neighbouring large towns. The old movement of hop pickers from the poorer districts of London to the hop-fields of Kent is a phenomenon of this sort. Hop cultivation was really only possible in those Kentish districts because of the availability of this temporary labour at the right time when the hop gardens provided a paid holiday for the whole family in late summer.

At the present day there are two particularly interesting aspects of the socio-economic factors. One is that with the increased standard of living the wife is no longer content to live in the isolated country cottage with none of the amenities enjoyed by her kinsfolk in the neighbouring town. Not unnaturally she demands electric light and the advantages which electricity can give in so many other directions – notably now with television; she demands running water and, perhaps less important, though still significant, main drainage. Although loneliness may have disappeared to some extent with radio and television there is the modern tendency to congregate and the desire to live in a settlement, even if it is only a comparatively small village, rather than in isolation. This is recognized in the modern policy of building agricultural workers' cottages in groups associated with an existing settlement rather than encouraging further construction of the so-called tied cottages actually on the farms themselves.

Another very interesting phenomenon is that which is the direct result quite obviously of fluctuations in agricultural prices. As Cobbett recognized nearly 150 years ago, there are marginal lands which it pays to plough and crop in those times when prices are high, in what he called 'dear corn times'. When agricultural prices drop, the cultivation of such marginal lands is no longer economic unless some improved method of managing the land can be produced. The result is seen in what geographers and others know as the 'fluctuation of the moorland edge' – that is to say, the dividing line between cultivated or improved land in crops or grass and the open rough grazing of the moorland. In times of high agricultural prices the moorland edge is pushed higher and higher up the hillside and indifferent land is brought into enclosed fields and cultivated. In times when agricultural prices drop, much of this land is abandoned and the moorland edge comes lower and lower. Over an extended period of time there is a very interesting result. We find on comparing land-use in Britain at the present day with the time of the Land Utilisation Survey in the nineteen-thirties, the period of high farming in the eighteen-sixties and seventies, or going back 100 years or more into the eighteen-forties that the really good-quality lands have remained the whole time in intensive cultivation despite all economic vicissitudes. On the other hand, the intrinsically poor land, the mountain moorland, it has never paid to cultivate throughout the whole period. We find the maximum of change in the intermediate lands. This historical phenomenon is one which merits serious consideration by those who contend that there is really no serious national importance in attempting to conserve the good agricultural land. History is against them.

In recent years much use has been made of the words 'undeveloped' and 'under-developed' as applicable to certain parts of the world. Various meanings have been given to these words. Many economists use the word 'under-developed' in the sense in which it is really a measure of poverty. If the national income per head in a given country falls below a certain level, that country can be described as under-developed, and in fact, this criterion of under-development has been used in official circles for the receipt of American aid. This leads us to the rather illogical position of a country which is intensely crowded with people to such an extent that they can scarcely obtain sufficient sustenance to maintain life, even with the most intensive cultivation of their land – a position which applies in parts of India – and yet such a land is officially described as 'under-developed'. By way of contrast, one can imagine an Australia, with 3 million square miles in which not one single acre was cultivated, but, provided the population was using its minerals and other resources in such a way as to maintain people there at a high standard of living with a high income per head, the country would be officially described as developed, or at least could not be described as under-developed.

The geographer rather naturally thinks of the term under-development in a different sense. It implies the possession of physical resources not yet fully used or fully exploited, using the word exploited in the best possible sense, for the benefit of the inhabitants of the country. In this sense we think of the great under-developed countries, not only of Africa with its vast population, of South America with the vast territories of Brazil and the Argentine and so on, but we think possibly of the relatively low stage of productivity of parts of Canada waiting to be developed and parts of the United States which might be more fully used. In that sense they come under the category of the under-developed countries of the world. It is in such under-developed countries that we look for the more intensive study of land resources which shall, as elsewhere, lead to the more intelligent use and the more effective production of commodities of animal and vegetable origin through the work of the farmer, the stockman, and the forester.

It must not be forgotten that the world is passing at the present time through what may be called the New Agricultural Revolution. One phase of this, rapidly increasing mechanization, is apparent to all. Another phase is chemicalization, the enormously increased use of chemical fertilizers, of insecticides and weed killers and of injections for animals. Geneticists, too, are evolving varieties of food plants and strains of animals designed to yield better and larger supplies of human food. With animals, artificial insemination is now being used extensively to this end.

CHAPTER 7

Land Planning

IN essence land planning is the right and balanced allocation of land between rival claimants. In crowded countries, especially those to which the adjective 'over-populated' may be applied in the sense that their land can no longer produce sufficient food to support their population, land is the commodity in short supply. Each rival claimant may present a good case, yet each may well be required to lower its requirements in the interest of the community as a whole, that is, in the national interest. Shortage of land dominates physical planning in Britain. In England and Wales there is only 0·8 acre per head of population of land of all sorts to satisfy all the varied needs of the people. In such circumstances there should be no such thing as 'waste land' – every part should be performing some function in the national economy. The planner's task is to determine the optimum use, in the national interest, of every acre of the surface. Indeed, his task goes further. Many acres of land can serve more than one purpose, as when hill moorland is used as a gathering ground for a water supply, pasture for sheep, and is also open of access for walkers seeking air and exercise. Multiple use of land must be promoted whenever possible.

Given that land planning must start from the present position and should be based on a careful, objective, and detailed survey and interpretation of that present position, what basic needs of mankind must be satisfied by a proper use of land?

There are at least six such basic needs of man which involve the use of land for their satisfaction. We may list them as food, shelter, work, recreation, movement, and security. Wherever population is dense, these become *competing* demands.

We see here the contrast between, for example, Britain and the United States. Whilst in certain limited areas there may be as strong competition for land in the United States as anywhere, the overall position is different. Each citizen of the United States can lay claim to some 12½ acres or about sixteen times as much as an Englishman. Many needs can be satisfied almost regardless of land requirements. Thus motor highway construction may be limited by finance but not by any overall shortage of land. Vast areas of the United States are just waste land as far as any present production is concerned. This can be seen even along the main lines from New York to Washington, whilst over much of New England farmland cleared at a vast expenditure of labour by the Pilgrim Fathers and subsequent generations has now become submarginal and reverted to second-growth scrub or woodland.

To return now to Britain, by far the greater part of our open land is used, directly or indirectly, for the production of food and raw materials. In this sense we may say that land not used for other purposes is being farmed or serves productive forestry. The development of other uses of land, such as for industry or housing or recreation or roadmaking, cuts into the remaining farmland, which consequently shows a continuous and somewhat alarming diminution in area. Because it may be argued that agriculture seeks to conserve open land for food production, whilst other uses result in its transfer and usually its closure, the unfortunate idea has grown up that there is an antagonism between 'town' and 'country' in planning. In reality the two are essentially complementary: the task is to plan the whole national estate in the national interest.

Undoubtedly the prior claimant to allocation of land is industry. The first need of man is work. Britain in particular depends on the maintenance of its manufacturing industry and export trade for its very existence, and this has become a highly competitive world. An industry can only survive provided it enjoys all the physical advantages, particularly right location, which it can possibly be afforded. For purposes of studying the problem of industrial location, the Scott Committee (the Committee on Land Utilization in Rural Areas) adopted a simple classification of industry into heavy, light, linked, and servicing industries.

The heavy industries include the extractive industries,

Fig. 9. Empty areas of the north-eastern United States

notably coal-mining, iron-ore mining, and quarrying. Obviously these are tied in their location by the occurrence of the mineral, and so cannot be located at will, whatever the planner may wish. As regards minerals there are those relatively valuable minerals of which, in due course, a country may require to develop and extract its total resources. In the case of Britain, coal, iron ore, metalliferous ores, mineral.

67

oil, and china clay may be cited as coming into this category, and provision must be made for the extraction of the mineral, however much the land may be wanted for other purposes. The emphasis should not be on *prevention* of working, but on restoration of the land to serve some other purpose after working.

On the other hand, there are many economic minerals in such abundant supply that we shall never use all our resources. We shall never use all our chalk and other limestone for lime, cement, and other purposes. We shall never use all our clay for making bricks and tiles and drainpipes. We shall never use all our sand for building or our gravel for concrete-making. Hence industries using these raw materials can be the subject of deliberately planned location. But such minerals are of low value in proportion to bulk and weight. For gravel delivered on a building site the greater part of the cost is in the transport, and the same is true of road stone, and even of cement and lime. Often only the technical expert can detect small differences in the raw material that render one part of a large mineral deposit much more valuable than another. The angularity of grain makes one sand valuable for building, whereas one that appears precisely similar to the layman has rounded grains, or it may be some obnoxious constituent renders it quite unsuitable. Very considerable weight must accordingly be given to the views of the technical expert in locating the extractive industries even of widespread mineral deposits, but the 'expert' is sometimes inclined to bluff for reasons other than those openly expressed.

In any case, however, the extractive industries are tied to the areas where Nature has placed the minerals. There are no means of placing a coalfield where one has not already been placed by Nature as a result of the long and complex geological history of the earth. It is man's task to locate the minerals, often skilfully hidden by Nature, but he cannot find what is not there. Yet these simple and obvious facts seem not infrequently ignored in our planning. No mineral working in a national park, we hear. Sometimes an historical monument can only be saved by sterilizing the mineral deposit on which it stands, but this is a very different matter from deliberately sterilizing a valuable resource by planning and building a new town on it. Yet to my knowledge suggestions have been made within recent decades to do this very thing.

Closely allied to the extractive industries are those heavy industries which are often dependent on them – iron smelting and making of steel; the making of bricks, tiles, earthenware, coarse pottery, and cement. Where the raw material is heavy, bulky, and of low value per unit of weight, or where there is a large proportion of waste in the process of manufacture, it is obviously uneconomic to transport the raw material more than a minimum distance from its origin. This is the reason for the establishment, fully justified, of the towns of Scunthorpe and Corby in the once quiet agricultural countryside of Lincolnshire and the Midlands.

Another obvious example of a location closely delimited by physical conditions is that of shipbuilding. The numerous little ports once devoted to the building of ships have faded away in face of the superior physical conditions, and especially the possibility of adaptation to changing requirements of ever-increasing size of ships enjoyed by Clydeside, Tyneside, Belfast, and Barrow. A special emphasis must be placed on the words 'changing requirements'. Each generation in turn seems to envisage a permanence of industrial development and invariably demands that a dying industry be kept alive unnaturally by shots in the arm of subsidies or protective tariffs.

Other industries, notably those in Britain which depend especially on import of raw materials and export of finished products, demand highly specialized sets of conditions for their location. A good example is that of petroleum refining – deep tide-water for receiving importing tankers: an element of danger and noxious smells keeping refineries away from city centres, and the answer is often a conflict with rural amenities. The Portland Cement industry needs limestone of the right character, clay of the right character, a waterside location for export, whilst the dust produced results in the classification of the industry as noxious. Suitable sites are restricted, but with such a heavy and bulky product land haulage is expensive, and hence the need for works serving each major region.

Many modern industries are complex in the extreme and either require close linkage between small specialist firms

Fig. 10. The location of the principal oil refineries of Britain; numerous pipelines are under construction

(this is well seen in the Birmingham area) or large integrated units involving a large labour supply. In this we see why the large town supplies the only answer – both in labour supply and the important local market. Similarly, before launching out into wider fields, a new industry trying out a new product or process would choose a large concentrated market where initial success could be achieved. We see herein one of the great natural attractions of London.

The servicing industries – gas, electricity, water supply,

retail trading, local transport, motor repairing, and so on – are obviously linked closely with the areas where the customers reside: the big town grows snowball fashion.

It will be seen that the number of industries which can be located at will is in fact strictly limited. Light industries which would seem to be 'footloose' and capable of locating themselves or being directed to new towns or to revivify existing old towns are in fact not numerous. Many which, at first sight, could be located anywhere will be found to have special needs, such as a very large water supply, or water of a special character, which further restrict location. The Scott Report gave reasons for regarding the rural village and open country in general as unsuitable for the location of industry, though stressing the valuable results of using existing or new small towns as sites for new plants.

The second great need of man is shelter – a home – and this raises the complex question of the provision of housing. If we accept the basic principle that the purpose of planning is not only to make the best use of resources but also to satisfy as fully as possible the needs and desires of the people, we must first ask: What sort of homes do the people want? A little reflection will suggest that the simple democratic principle of taking a vote on the matter is inadequate, because the range of experience of the voters is limited to what exists. It is difficult for the average man or woman to visualize, as an architect would do, entirely new types of home. If we accept the verdict, therefore, of the popular vote, it would seem that the Englishman likes a detached home with a small individual garden, fenced off from his neighbours, where he is king of the castle. The semi-detached comes next in favour, the terrace house, maisonnette, or flat well down the list. The individual home with the individual garden – open density housing at, say, twelve houses to the acre – means in the first place the use of much land, in the second place high costs in the provision of gas, electricity, water supply, sewerage, public transport, and so on. In the third place, the distance from home to work soon becomes a serious problem in effort, time, and money.

Care must be exercised in talking about density of housing. In the bad old days of the early part of the Industrial Revolution back-to-back houses of two storeys were so crowded together that as many as 120 to the acre were built. If one takes the average size of the family in those days as five persons, this would represent no less than 600 persons per acre actually living on the ground. Modern standards are very different. If we attempt to provide the single detached house which a survey would show the people seem

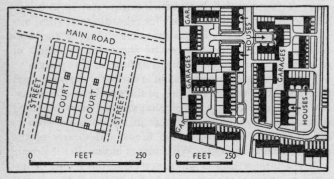

Fig. 11. Contrasts between old and new in housing layouts. The plan on the left is double the scale of that on the right, yet each little box of the back-to-back houses was intended as a family home

to desire, then at sixteen houses to the acre it is only possible to provide quite a small garden. It is true that very many people in Britain enjoy a garden in which their children can play, and also take a pride in growing flowers with, provided it is sufficiently large, vegetables which help not inconsiderably in the family budget. Sixteen houses to the acre gives but a small space for any cultivation, and so the modern tendency is to aim at ten or twelve houses to the acre. When the Land Utilisation Survey of Britain was working it had to draw an arbitrary line between houses with small gardens or backyards which were not likely to be used for the production of vegetables, and those which had gardens sufficiently large to be productive of fruit, flowers, and vegetables. It was found that the limit was something in the order of twelve houses per acre. More than twelve houses, no production; less than twelve houses, some production. If we take the modern family as 3·5 per household, and the density of twelve houses per acre, this gives forty-two persons actually living on the acre. A calculation based on dwellings per acre rather ignores the fact of size of dwellings – two-bedroomed, three-bedroomed, and four-bedroomed houses each have their needs – so that perhaps a more useful method of measuring density is by 'habitable rooms' per acre, for which purpose one takes the bedrooms, and the living rooms, excluding the kitchen, bathroom, and 'usual offices'. Town planners are now accustomed to measure the degree of crowding or overcrowding by persons per habitable room. The standard they adopt is one person per habitable room; more is regarded as overcrowding.

We can indulge in some interesting speculations based upon these simple figures. Taking the population of England and Wales as 46 million, if the people were all accommodated on what we might call standard density – forty-two persons per acre – it would mean that more than 1 million acres would be required for housing alone. Housing density is not the whole story, because it is not really possible to separate housing or net density from the density of what we may call the living space as a whole, or gross density. There is obviously a great difference between an arrangement whereby houses are separated from one another by narrow roads, just wide enough for two lines of traffic, and one where they are placed in the open layout of a garden city, with broad roads having grass verges, pavements for pedestrians, and perhaps lined with trees. Similarly, very closely associated with the actual housing is the provision of adequate space for the other needs of the people – their social needs – for example, parks, recreational areas for mothers with children and for old people, the playing-fields for the young people and adults, the large extent of land which is required by schools for children, and then the requirements of the shopping areas, the recreational areas, the business areas – all needs, in fact, which go to make up the ordinary life of the community. We get then the concept of gross density of the area required for a balanced town. In some older towns density on this basis may be very high, and we can contrast these with some of the new towns which are actually being built. In these an open layout has generally been adopted, and so the overall density accepted for Crawley New Town, for example, is less than ten persons per acre. This means that a planned town of 50,000 persons will require altogether some 6,000 acres or nearly 10 square miles. The overall density adopted in Harlow is twelve to thirteen per acre. The designated area is 6,320 acres, or about $3\frac{1}{4}$ miles north to south and $4\frac{1}{2}$ east to west. The planned population has been increased from 60,000 to 80,000 to provide for a better-balanced community.

There has been much argument as to what constitutes the ideal size for a town, that is if one is deliberately planning a new community. There is perhaps a tendency to think in terms of 50,000 or 60,000 up to 100,000; for a community of this size it is possible to provide a full range of social amenities, including for example a live theatre, which could scarcely be supported by a smaller community; it is also possible to have a range of specialist shops, and it is likely that the size of religious communities will be such as to support a church of their own denomination. The New Towns which are being built in Britain are therefore being planned to accommodate something like this number of people. Let us look at a town of 60,000 such as we have visualized with an open density. Covering as it does an area of nearly 10 square miles, it requires little calculation to show that such a town if more or less circular would be some 3 miles across, and that people living on the periphery – on the margin – would have a distance of $1\frac{1}{2}$ miles to reach the shopping or the civic centre in the heart. If, as may be desirable, the industrial area is situated on one margin, it means that there must be a journey of something like 3 miles from the opposite side of the town to the factory area. More than this and one begins to lose the advantage of a new community in the difficulty of traffic congestion, the time taken to get to one's work, and so on. Britain almost more than any other country in the world must seriously face the problem of building upwards: that is to say of accommodating a considerable proportion of its population in high blocks of flats. It is said that the Englishman is averse to this type of existence, but, if the case is such, he does in fact differ from the inhabitants of most countries of the world today. In the past our own blocks of flats have been associated with the lower-income groups and they have lacked the obvious amenities, such as central heating, constant hot-water supply, electrically operated lifts from top to bottom, and so on, as well as such details, important notwithstanding, as easy facilities for disposal of dust and rubbish and storage places for prams on the ground floor, playgrounds for children on the top of the buildings, and drying grounds for washing. It is likely that the controversy regarding flats versus individual houses will continue to rage for a long time as far as Britain is concerned. And it is unfortunate that there should be hot feelings on both sides whenever this subject is raised. Those who oppose the building of flats base their case primarily on the presumption that everyone prefers an individual home and garden and on the high cost per unit of accommodation. The latter ignores the higher cost of providing full services to a scattered community and the cost in both money and time of the journey to work for the suburban dweller.

A compromise would seem to be obvious. Surely a person in the course of life is likely to live in at least four homes, which may be of somewhat different types. There is in the first instance the home in which one's parents live, in which one perhaps is born, and lives one's childhood. One has as a rule no greater degree of choice over this than one has over the choice of one's parents. It is in the later teenages that the desire for independence grows quite naturally, the student at College, whether male or female, develops naturally a desire to live a life of his or her own, and searches for that which is virtually unobtainable in most of the cities of

Britain, a tiny self-contained flat of a couple of rooms at the most – a bedroom, a sitting-room-study, with a bathroom and small kitchen. Quite frequently there comes the stage when two students will share such quarters, or when the idea grows that two can live as cheaply as one, and the young husband and wife – perhaps, both studying, both working – want accommodation very much of this character. They certainly have no desire at that stage for a larger house with the responsibilities of a garden, nor does the wife wish to be separated from the job which she has undertaken or her studies – the great desire of both partners is to be as near as possible to the daily occupation, and especially to be near the centre of the town, where may be found so many of the amenities desired in youth and early manhood – the cinema, the live theatre, perhaps art galleries, and concert halls and library, college, or night school. Unfortunately many students are compelled to waste an immense amount of time in getting to their work; one sees them strap-hanging in the tube, trying to study at the same time. Surely this could be obviated by building blocks of flats especially for young people near their work.

Many others would if they could live near their work. Take those who are concerned with the running of London's hotels and restaurants, theatres and cinemas, who cannot finish work until late at night. What a joy to be able, as it were, to tumble into bed, without the necessity of worrying about last trains home. It would seem that a compromise in all cases is to build blocks of flats near the centre of the town so that those who wish could live in them and be near their work or pleasure, as the case may be.

The third stage, requiring the third type of accommodation, comes rather naturally with the arrival of the family. The wife gives up her job, devotes her life to the occupation of motherhood, when for the benefit of the children's health space and fresh air are desirable. At this stage in life there is so much to be said for the garden, where the husband coming home during the week-end can himself gain advantages to health and strength by working about the house or garin winter in the neighbourhood of London rises only 15° above the horizon. Thus a tall building casts a long shadow, and it is important that tall blocks of flats should be widely separated and so arranged that as far as possible none of them lacks light and air. Questions of overall density still persist, and it is far more important that here, in contrast, say, to Italy or even New York, high buildings, especially blocks of flats, should be surrounded by adequate open space. For such purposes 'open space' can include railway sidings and goods yards, and is provided also by a stretch of river, such as the Thames. Unfortunately there has been in some towns the tendency to interpret this question of density far too narrowly, as when the L.C.C. prevented the Borough of Paddington from building high experimental blocks and refused to count Paddington goods sidings as open space.

No doubt has been left in the mind of the reader that there is in Britain and in many other countries an overall shortage of land. There is particularly a shortage of good agricultural land capable of producing food; and so the general principle has come to the fore that, other things being equal, we should avoid building on good agricultural land and should seek to conserve as much as possible for food production. This would seem logically to lead to two things. The first is to try to select the poorer qualities of land for the siting of our new towns or extensions of existing towns. The second would be to regard very open densities, such as ten persons to the acre, as being an extravagance which we really cannot afford in this country, and to look therefore for higher densities. Both these trends have caused a tremendous amount of opposition among certain groups. Taking the second point first, it is certainly true that the amount of land which would be saved by building to a higher density is not large, and the advocacy for flats, for greater density, is not therefore to be based primarily upon the question of saving agricultural land: it is based on the provision of greater amenities for the occupants, especially the shortening of the journey to work, which we have just mentioned in the preceding paragraphs. The question, however, of the type of land on which to build is another story. It has given rise to what has now become known as the great garden controversy. What is in fact quite a simple issue has been made unnecessarily complicated. The simple issue is this – that if one takes a given tract of open land and plans and builds thereon a new settlement of garden-city type, it can be shown by measurement of land that because of the large area taken up by roads, pathways, verges, the houses themselves, their garages, the garden paths which lead to them – the actual area of land left which is capable of being cultivated and producing fruit or flowers or vegetables must obviously be limited. In those cases where it has been measured with some care it is found that something between 15 and 25 per cent remains. We can say therefore that only one-fifth of the land which is occupied by a garden-city type of settlement actually remains available for cultivation. The argument that the individual garden cultivator gets more from a given piece of land than would be obtained on the same type of land by a professional market gardener is not borne out by such limited statistics as are available. Therefore even an open-density housing estate can only produce one-fifth of the food the same land would produce as a market garden. This would seem to be quite obvious. It is, however, pointed out that not only do fresh vegetables from one's own garden have special virtues which it is difficult to estimate, but also in terms of cash they represent a very considerable saving to the house-wife as well as a considerable contribution in aggregate to the national larder. Calculations based on retail prices of vegetables naturally give some very high figures of the value of produce per acre. There are those who have then compared these figures with the average output of ordinary farm-land. Quite clearly this is not comparing like with like. If one wants to take the intensive production of gardens one should surely compare it with land which is being intensively cultivated, for example in market gardens, and one must either take the wholesale price, the market price of the produce in the two cases, or the retail price. To take the retail price in the case of gardens and to compare this with an overall production of farm crops at farm gate prices is obviously very far from comparing like with like. The position is, of course, complicated by the absence of transport and handling costs in the case of garden produce.

Another very important point with regard to the avoidance of good agricultural land for development is that what may be the best land from an agricultural point of view may be very far from being the best where the construction of houses with gardens is concerned. Really first-class agricultural land, which we shall discuss in a later chapter, would most likely be a fine loam with a considerable proportion of clay (so that it holds moisture well) and probably rich in organic matter which would cause it to have a black or very dark brown colour. The result is a dark and sticky mould. Now in a garden this of course would be very fertile, but from the housewife's point of view has the drawback of clinging to the shoes of the husband or the children and of causing a great deal of dirt to be brought into the house. Moreover, a husband may have only Saturday afternoons or Sundays to cultivate his garden, and on such land it is a sticky and a dirty business and heavy work after rain. By way of contrast if a housing estate is located on light sandy soil, which dries very quickly after rain, the children can play in the garden quite soon after even heavy rain; the sand does not cling so easily to shoes, does not make the same amount of mess in the house, and from the housewife's point of view is relatively clean dirt. Such land can be fed with manures so as to be extremely productive of vegetables, and it has the advantage of being very easily worked. The wife can do the weeding with little effort, the husband can do his digging at any time of the year, and in any state of the weather. Such land does not necessarily have a full range of flowers – it will probably grow rhododendron, azalea, and many of the heath plants extremely well, though it may be heartbreaking to the man who is very fond of his bed of roses. Thus light land which the farmer would call too hungry can easily be made into a garden requiring a minimum of work for maintenance. Another type of land not very well suited for housing is heavy clay, as any readers of this book will know who have gardens situated on such land. Yet clay soils afford some of the finest pasture-lands, as well as providing some of the richest cornlands of this country. There is therefore a considerable advantage to the householder in going on to the poorer land, which does not rob the country to any extent of its productive capacity. We may go so far as to say that some of the most favoured residential areas in the British Isles literally owe their character to their poor, light, sandy soil. A very good case of this sort is Bournemouth, the original site of which was due to poor cheap land which had never attracted the farmer. The favoured heathlands of Surrey, on the margins of which there are many areas of attractive housing, are other examples of the advantage of siting housing on poor land.

Before leaving housing and housing density, a word must be said about allotments. Allotments may be regarded as a man's garden away from his home, and available to those who wish to cultivate and produce flowers and vegetables, but where there is no compunction on those who prefer to occupy their leisure in other ways. It has been urged that allotments should be so arranged as to be very close to the houses in which the holders live, but this was combated in evidence which was given to the Scott Committee. Some of the allotment holders then claimed that they liked their allotments far enough away from the house for them not to be at the beck and call of their wives when they were wanting to have a quiet pipe (with a minimum of work) on a Saturday afternoon. As a rule a great deal of hand work goes into the preparation of the soil in an allotment. If the land is heavy, allotment holders will feed it with ashes and lighten it and spend their spare shillings on manures to render its fertility high. Even poor land which has been worked intensively in this way becomes so changed in character as to be very fertile. Usually it is little short of criminal for local authorities (the chief offenders) to choose old allotment gardens for a housing estate. A great sacrifice is incurred by those who have worked the allotments and brought them up to the state of perfection which is so often attained, and it is little compensation to be given new raw land. It is for this reason that the Ministry of Agriculture is very much on the side of allotment holders in helping them to keep their land and to prevent it from being used for housing and other purposes.

It will be clear from what has just been said that very many considerations will enter into the choice of land for the extension of housing around a town, and particularly for the site of a new town. Naturally the quality of soil is only one factor to be considered.

We come now to the third of the basic needs of mankind where land is concerned, and that is land for recreation. It is quite wrong to regard recreation, as perhaps some of our ancestors did, as a luxury for the favoured few. With the increasing amount of leisure which is characteristic of the modern world it is important to use that leisure wisely. In this connexion the maintenance of the health of the nation, both physical and mental, links up very closely with the availability of land for recreation. Land for recreation must be considered at several different levels. Young children in towns, with or without their mothers, need a public park or recreation ground which must be close to the home. The demand is for small units widely distributed throughout housing areas, where children are safe to play away from traffic, otherwise they will use the street outside their home. The second stage is the actual playing-field. But the town park is also used by the elderly as well as by those who seek to snatch a few quiet minutes from office, home, or shopping. Best results are achieved when the different types of recreational area are kept separate, but requirements of land rise accordingly. Something of the order of 7 to 10 acres per 1,000 of population is a desirable minimum.

Sport is inseparable from British concepts of education. The town school three or four storeys high (partly surrounded by an old asphalted playground) has given place to a school with a sprawling horizontal layout all on one or at most two floors and set in a considerable stretch of playing-fields. In the latter part of the Second World War the Ministry of Education came down in favour of a minimum of 13 acres, which was itself a reduction from 15 acres, for new secondary schools. In view of the country's limited land resources the question arises whether this is not unnecessarily extravagant, besides giving many of our headmasters and headmistresses a real headache in maintenance problems.

The need for playing-fields does not end with schooldays. It is a vital requirement for the youth of the nation past school age. If one accepts a standard of 6 or 7 acres per 1,000 of population, 360 acres – over half a square mile – would be needed for a town of 60,000. It should be noted that this requirement, so closely associated with the work of the National Playing Fields Association, is quite apart from that of sports grounds for entertainment – for professional football, and cricket teams.

In the British countryside, sport has played a great role and is traditionally associated with the village green. It is perhaps unfortunate that modern standards require the separate recreation ground even in villages, whereas the loan of a farmer's field for a couple of afternoons a week was deemed adequate in the past.

Then there is also a demand for land for recreation, quite apart from that which is near at hand. We think in terms of the green belt of open land, not necessarily for recreation only, to be conserved around our towns. We think in terms of considerable acreages required for games such as golf. But it is for walking and exercising the dog and picnicking that we value the common lands come down to us from the days when they were the wastelands of the Lord of the Manor. Though there is no legal right of access to many of them, in the lowlands and near towns they are primarily used for such purposes. Changes have taken place in our need of more extensive land for recreation: greater mobility of more

and more people has resulted in the demarcation of tracts
of scenically beautiful open land as national parks. Some
young people, it is true, still like to ramble, but Britain,
like most other countries of the world, is rapidly becoming
a nation of car-owners. As soon as a man becomes a car-
owner he tends to lose the natural use of his lower limbs;
he will go wherever he can drive the car, but rarely walks
far from it. But the car can tow a caravan, and with this
there is a new demand for caravan sites for holidays. Just
in time we have realized the need for the open land to be
conserved round the coasts. In planning for recreation it
is obvious that town and country interests become closely
interwoven, and the rights of the townsman in the countryside are now widely recognized. But we should notice that
land for recreation such as that in National Parks is not to
be regarded as exclusively for such purposes. It is here that
the multi-purpose use of land is of paramount significance
and importance. In the selection of the larger areas for recreational purposes there are two criteria, the first being the
natural beauty, the second the poor quality in the land,
which renders it unfit for farming in an intensive way, and
therefore entailing little sacrifice to the country in leaving it
open and primarily accessible to walkers. There is also a
very different use of land which perhaps can be included
under the general heading of recreation. It is land for the
conservation of our native wild flora and fauna. A quite
surprising number of people in this country find tremendous
joy in observing the habits of animals and birds – the bird-
watchers are innumerable – and the amateur botanist, who
is not necessarily a collector of plants, but one who likes to
observe plants in their natural habitat, is by no means a
rarity. Side by side with the National Parks Commission
we now have the Nature Conservancy, and numerous areas
in Britain have been set aside as Nature Reserves. Often of
course it is necessary to limit public access to such areas
very strictly, and hence the distinction from National Parks,
which are recreational. In countries where there are very
large areas of land available, National Parks themselves

primarily of roads and airfields. The era of railway expansion we must regard, broadly speaking, as past. It is unlikely that we shall see here any considerable extension of our railway network. The opposite is indeed the case, for many branch lines are being closed down, though, on the other hand, extensions of railway sidings or marshalling yards may take up more land. But by and large the problem of land for railways and the severance or splitting up of farms which it caused in the past is something which does not bother us seriously for the future.

Road development is another matter. Our road system was planned originally by the Romans, and it is an amazing tribute to their wisdom in national planning that most of the roads they aligned nearly 2,000 years ago have persisted and proved useful right down to the present day. Indeed, if we look at a road map of Britain, we shall see that almost the only straight roads are those which were planned deliberately by the Romans that long time ago. The Anglo-Saxons who followed them were essentially farmers. They were much more concerned with getting from their villages to their farms and their farms to their fields. Often the roads resulted from the chance joining up of field ways, and hence the very irregular pattern of winding lanes still characteristic of much of our road system.

In any case neither the roads themselves nor the road system of Britain were designed to take modern high-speed motor traffic or modern heavy-tonnage lorries. In a new country, where roads have not yet been completed, the problem is a simple one – roads can be designed for modern conditions. But what is the position in a country like Britain, very densely settled, where in fact all parts of the country suitable for farming have been used for centuries; where there is an age-old network of farms, hamlets, villages, towns, and cities? Up to the present we have relied mainly on trying to alter the existing roads to meet the new conditions, by widening, to some extent by straightening, by constructing bypasses where there are bottlenecks through villages and towns. The result is not by any means wholly satisfactory. One can go for perhaps a few miles, for example along the Great North Road, and find it adequate in width, and then the inevitable bottleneck arises where widening is virtually impossible because of numerous buildings on either side. A bypass round a village often has the effect of cutting farm buildings off from the farm fields and crossing innumerable lanes. Further, tradition is very strong in Britain, and the tradition as well as the law is that the King's Highway, or the Queen's Highway, is for the use of all citizens equally without let or hindrance. We have every right to drive a flock of sheep down the middle of a main highway. It is now necessary to face the new position, and present declared policy is to construct a small number of main high-speed motorways restricted to motor traffic. Of course other countries have done this: the *Autobahnen* of Germany are well known. But even Germany has not the congestion of population which has to be faced in Britain. However, a start has been made and great publicity attended the opening of the first motorway, near Preston, in 1959, and later of the M1.

In this new road programme there are three outstanding aspects to be considered. The first is to secure the maximum efficiency from the new roads, the second is to cause the least possible disturbance to existing uses and users of land, and the third is to safeguard the heritage of beauty which is such an important part of the life of the country.

Taking these in order, the new concept is something quite different from the old. Our old roads joined village with village, village with town, town with city. Our new roads should on the whole avoid passing through any settlement. They should go through the least-populated parts of the country, but at the same time should have ready access to important towns on the route. A map is appended which shows some of the roads which have been proposed. Quite clearly a number are important new lines of communication. There is certainly a need for one new main highway from south to north, with probably the London Docks as a starting point, right away through to Scotland, avoiding the great cities and towns on the way, but having easy access to

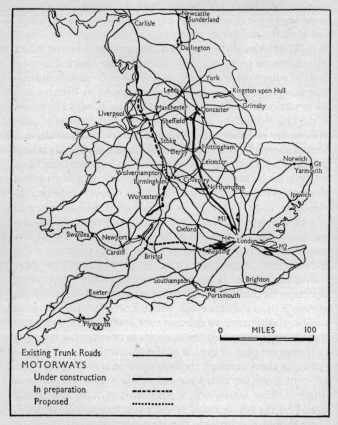

Fig. 14. The trunk roads of Britain and proposed motorways

them. The M4, London to South Wales, is under construction, with a Severn bridge. The present absurdity is that it is
only possible to reach that great industrial area by the cir-
cuit northwards across the river Severn at Gloucester, with
the narrow streets and the unsatisfactory ring road which is
involved in passing that city. Similarly it is quite a stagger-

ing thing that the great city and port of Kingston-upon-Hull has no direct communication southwards because of the existence of the Humber.

At first sight it would seem satisfactory to take a census of existing traffic as an indication of roads which are needed. One must bear in mind, however, that many roads are avoided because of their present characters – perhaps narrow, winding, and hilly – so that the present volume of traffic is little indication of that which would develop along an adequate highway. In this connexion it is interesting to note that a new main road has been proposed from north to south of Wales, to link up what are at present rather isolated parts of the principality, and to unite north, south, and centre. It has been pointed out that there is practically no traffic which goes from north to south in Wales. Of course there is not: there is no road by which it can go. Thus in certain cases one has to rely on what may be called a hunch or an intelligent guess as to roads which are really needed.

Now we come to the character of the roads. We must not only think of the present, but try to visualize the future, and it would seem obvious that at least we must have highways with up and down lanes. Two lanes each way? No, probably the need for three is indicated when one thinks in terms of the relatively slow and heavy lorry traffic, fast bus traffic, as well as private cars. Then there must be the usual rules which apply in other countries – no stopping on the actual highway, but the provision of adequate 'laybys' where traffic can draw off. There is the question of dazzle at night, and hence the desirability of a central verge. In fact it is very often of advantage for the up and down lanes not only to be separated from one another, but on a different level. If there is a verge between the two, it should be of minimum width of at least 16 feet – the length of a modern large car in turning from one lane into the other. Even this is somewhat inadequate for lorry traffic. It will be seen that the total width involved is quite considerable, more especially as one needs also grass verges or land on either side not only for the provision of laybys, but also for another reason. A dead-straight road with long, straight fences on either side produces a feeling of monotony which is not only undesirable aesthetically, but causes sleepiness among drivers, resulting in serious accidents. Hence varied irregular hedgerows rather than a post-and-wire fence, clumps of trees, and so on are desirable. The net result is the use of a very large area of land. It involves for a main highway of six lanes a total width of about 120 feet using up 15 acres per mile. Then there is the problem of cross-roads. In a country where shortage of land is not a problem – for example, the United States – one can have the elaborate clover-leaf and figure-of-eight junctions where traffic leaving or joining the main highway can do so without actually stopping for lights or roundabouts. But many of these clover-leaf junctions take up something like a square mile, or 640 acres of land. Apart from the question of cost, this is an extravagance which we can scarcely consider in most parts of the British Isles. In any case road junctions must be reduced in number to a minimum, the existing roads being taken under or over the new highways by tunnels and bridges without joining them. The only obstacle here is one of expense.

Secondly, how can such modern motorways be fitted into the existing intricate pattern of land use in this country? As far as possible it is quite clear that they should use the poorer land, they should disturb existing farms as little as possible, and there is an advantage scenically and in the cost of land and other ways in taking them as far as possible over heath-land and moorland which is little used. Although, with the availability of modern earth-moving machinery, it is no longer necessary to follow the contours of the ground and the making of considerable cuttings or embankments presents few difficulties, the use of high moorland may not be desirable because of the prevalence of cloud and mist and fog in winter months. Especially in the north, there is the added trouble of winter snow. One may say, in fact, that there are probably three stages in the alignment of one such modern road. There is, first, the policy of roughly where the road must go; and, secondly, the engineering considerations as to the line which is most suited, and the crossing of various obstacles. There is, third, the adjustment, often quite small, which can be made to cause the least damage to farming, farm units, villages, and so on. Many of the proposed new roads have been already sketched out on this basis and their line agreed.

A third consideration is the fitting of these new highways into the existing pattern of the countryside. Lively interest in this question is displayed by such national bodies as the Roads Beautifying Association, the Councils for the Preservation of Rural England and Rural Wales. The C.P.R.E., in conjunction with the Automobile Association and other interested bodies, set up a joint committee which drew up a general scheme for the scenic treatment of new roads which was approved by the Ministry of Transport in 1954. Many different problems were considered – how best to fit the roads into the landscape; how best to avoid dazzle and other hazards by shrub and tree planting; how best to treat the verges. Beautifying by planting is a field of study almost on its own. Team work, representing a very wide variety of interests, is involved. What trees will grow in different circumstances? Should they be introduced or native? Care must be taken not to plant trees which carry pests and diseases, difficult to control; there are certain trees which are perhaps objectionable because of the leaves which they shed and which may cause a danger of skidding in the autumn months. Modern roads bring other problems, notably the possibility of the spread of weeds unless considerable expenditure is incurred in keeping the verges in order.

The traffic problem is almost universal. There is, indeed, a danger that the world will be over-populated by automobiles long before it is over-populated by people. In crowded Britain it is certain that we must face the sacrifice of a certain proportion of our remaining open land for new highways, quite apart from any needed for the widening and improvement of existing roads. There is another class of road which is becoming important here. Other countries have what they would call scenic or tourist highways, and it may be that to canalize the tourist traffic in such an area as the coastlands of Devon and Cornwall is desirable if we wish to preserve the byways which are at present so terribly congested. If we can canalize the main stream of tourist traffic, it will help to maintain the beauty and character of the countryside, rather than the reverse, which some people would fear.

Surprising as it may seem, there is also still a need for roads to open up or make accessible some of the remoter parts of Britain, particularly of the west coastal lands of Scotland, which are so attractive and so potentially important.

Some interesting planning problems are presented by Britain's canals. Most were constructed in the pre-railway era, when transport by indifferent roads was horse-drawn, slow, and expensive. A horse towing a barge could easily move forty times the load possible on a cart. The hilly if not mountainous nature of even Lowland Britain meant that very numerous locks were needed on the canals; the motive power for the barges was usually a single horse, so that long, narrow barges on narrow canals became standard, always with a towing path. Like other things, British canals were well built and intended to last, and so they have survived into an age when changed circumstances have made the canals a national problem. Although for carriage of goods they have been superseded by the railways, and latterly by the heavy lorry on the roads, canals can and do still serve a useful function, where they are large enough for power-driven barges, have but few locks, and serve populous centres, for bulk movement of heavy commodities such as coal. The majority were in due course acquired by the railways, sometimes conditionally on their being maintained, and so were nationalized with British Railways in 1947. Originally, no doubt, canals, like railways and modern motor roads, were condemned as unsightly gashes and scars across a pleasant countryside. Today they have become in many areas so much part of the essential rural pattern that their preservation is defended strenuously on amenity grounds – the easy, shady walk along the tow-path, the quiet fishing or boating – as well as the fact that they provide essential water supplies for farmers' cattle and sometimes are part of the field drainage system. Even where commercially used, public opinion is attracted mainly to the presumedly romantic nature of life on a barge and to the gay colours which happily many barge-owners still employ. Certainly canals form a fascinating example of the changing values which constantly face the physical planner.

Another modern use of land for transport purposes is for civil airports. The increasing size and weight of aircraft for long-distance operations involve a very large demand upon land. The need for runways in different directions according to the state of the winds is a factor which suggests that a large area of land has to be sterilized. A very good example of the difficulty was afforded when the Heathrow site was being selected for London's modern international airport. Previously London had relied on the inadequate resources of Croydon aerodrome and to some extent on Hendon, so that something really had to be done to find a large area. The choice fell upon the flat, well-drained, and magnificently productive market-garden land of south Middlesex – perhaps the finest remaining agricultural land in the whole of Britain. But there was the point – London had to have a first-class airport, and so, as a deliberate decision of national policy at Cabinet level, this very productive land was sacrificed in order to provide for the essential air communications of London. Again the problem is that of a closely settled country where sites available for airports are obviously limited. Though they must be reasonably near the towns they are to serve, it would seem to be an extravagance we cannot afford for each town to have its own airport. Although at present the increasing use of jet aircraft is introducing new problems of noise and length of runway, in the near future aircraft with a vertical take-off may render obsolete all our airports.

We turn now to a fifth use of land. We cannot enjoy these
various advantages unless we secure them, which means a
sacrifice of a certain amount of land to the needs of the
fighting services – the Army, the Navy, and the Air Force –
to which we may link, because of their interest in things like
nuclear development, other Ministries, such as Power,
Works, and Supply. The Army clearly needs land of various
types. There are the small areas situated near towns for bar-
racks and 'square bashing' and for the training of recruits.
It is clearly uneconomic to take small parties of men large
distances for their initial training. With our modern
mechanized army there is the need of practice land for use
by tanks and for the training of lorry drivers, and hence the
use of poor heathland in many parts of the country. The
War Office would doubtless claim that it needs land of this
type in each of the Commands. This is quite apart from the
demand for large tracts of land as battle-training areas, of
which we have several in this country. Artillery, anti-tank
exercises, and practice with live ammunition involve the use
of land as ranges. It is interesting that much of this work can
be done by firing out to sea, because a shell bursts as soon as
it touches the surface of the ocean, just as if it were touching
the surface of the land. Even this involves an arrangement
of shipping and fisheries for the purpose. It is unfortunately
only too obvious that heavy tanks and weapons do a considerable amount of damage to land, and sometimes War
Office use of land is incompatible with other uses. In other
cases land is only required for training purposes for short
periods of the year and other uses are possible. The problem
of the Air Force is a serious one because of the ever-increasing size and speed of planes, so that larger and larger airfields are required: this is a very serious demand on land.
Some service airfields are permanent and have a range of
permanent buildings associated with them; others are
required for defence purposes and are kept on a care-and-
maintenance basis in case they may be at some time
required. The Fleet Air Arm comes also into the picture in
this demand on land. The Air Force obviously needs bomb-

ing ranges – if these are to be on land, where are they to be? It is a difficult problem; and often in what seems to be wild and uninhabited areas there develops a conflict with the need to preserve the rarer flora and fauna of this country which can only survive in such remote areas. It is fortunately true that much of the training for our forces is carried out overseas where land is not in such short supply, but this is not a possibility when short periods of training are involved, or for secret experimentation which is often important. Apart from these demands, the Services also need a large number of small sites for radar stations. Rather naturally in time of war, as during the Second World War, the Fighting Services had virtually the last word as to what they required. In time of peace the position is somewhat different. It is argued that the Fighting Services are extravagant in their demands. Truly there was a time after the war when they were demanding for their own purposes an acreage which was found to total something like one-third of the whole of England, Wales, and Scotland – a demand which was obviously impossible to meet. While one would be quite willing to sacrifice for tank-training areas some of the wilder areas, for example, in the Highlands of Scotland, boggy land with deep peat would be quite unsuitable, indeed useless, for the purpose. We assume therefore that the sacrifice of considerable areas which are at present valuable land in other ways – the Isle of Purbeck, Dartmoor, and so on – is necessary for Service use. What are the essential minima for Service needs is a matter very difficult for the layman to judge, but it has to be fitted into the whole general picture. It is perhaps one of the defects of our present system of town and country planning that when land has been released to the War Office, the planning authority may see with dismay or disgust much of it used, not for military purposes, but for large enclosures for houses, or perhaps not being used at all. However, present indications are that as 'conventional' weapons become less important, in an age of nuclear warfare and hydrogen bombs, Service demands on land will become less. In the meantime our crowded island must provide space for bases manned by American or NATO forces.

We come now to the final use of land: for the production of foodstuffs and raw materials. It is strange, perhaps, to put this need last, since the first need of mankind is undoubtedly food. But under the national economy we have developed much of our food is obtained from overseas. As a great manufacturing and commercial nation we have put industry first. Although we have suggested there is no basic conflict between town and country planning, it must be admitted that the five essential uses of land we have just indicated – land for industry, land for homes, land for recreation, land for communications, and land for defence – all tend to bite into what is at present the open land of the country available for the production of food and raw materials by the farmer and the forester. The total area of England and Wales is only 36 million acres, and it was alarm at the rate at which the open land was passing to other uses which caused the Government to set up the Scott Committee in the nineteen-forties. In the inter-war years open land was being lost at something between 50,000 and 70,000 acres a year. One only needs to look at this over a period of, say, twenty years to realize that in that period something between a million and $1\frac{1}{4}$ million acres passed from farming and forestry to other uses.

Despite the fact that we now have a comprehensive system of town and country planning, the change goes on, and must of necessity go on. There is some doubt as to the rate at which land is currently being lost from farming and forestry to other purposes. It cannot very well be less than 35,000 acres a year in England and Wales, and probably exceeds that figure. Over the whole period 1939–58 the land formerly open, in farming or forestry, and transferred to other uses certainly exceeds 1,000,000 acres in England and Wales alone. It can be argued that this post-war change is for the good, being due to the provision of better-quality housing with larger gardens, and that, as the rate of population increase slows down, the demand will become much less or almost cease, and we may even reach a static position. But there is no doubt at the present time that the continued urbanization, which is perhaps the best word to use, which is taking place in Britain is a very real threat to our land resources. Every farm in this country is in a certain sense a factory. It has a balance of land of different types, it has a balance of units in the form of fields, which are requisite to its economic working, yet so often the planner who is trained purely as a town planner fails to realize that he cannot lop 30 acres off a farm and still expect that farm to work as an economic unit. Its buildings and layout are geared to a farm of a certain size, and it might even be better to take the whole for development rather than to take fragments, as is so often done by planning authorities. Some of the difficulties have been overcome, as will be described in a later chapter, by careful collaboration between the Ministries responsible – the Ministry of Housing and Local Government for town planning, the Ministry of Agriculture, Fisheries and Food for production of food from the ground. We shall consider in Chapter 11 some of the special problems in agriculture, but we may note here some of the major ones.

One is to conserve the better qualities of land, not only because of the initially higher productivity and returns, but also because the return from expenditure on management, including fertilizers, is greater if the expenditure is made on intrinsically good land. It is quite wrong to think that one can upgrade poor qualities of land, for example, land with only 3 or 4 inches of soil over rock, to anything like that of the highest quality. Second, and sometimes almost as important, is the conservation of the good farm units – those which are well laid out and which have adequate farm buildings for their size. A third consideration is adequate integration between hill farming, particularly for sheep, and afforestation. The old conflict which existed in the early days of the Forestry Commission has now been largely eliminated by mutual good will and the unifying function of the Minister of Agriculture responsible also for forestry.

It is important to remember that agriculture, because of the number it employs, is the greatest industry in the country, with the exception perhaps of the tourist industry. In England and Wales there are something like 300,000 farmers, and the number of those directly dependent on the land is approximately 5 per cent of our total population. This is of course apart from those whose main livelihood is supplying the essential services to this rural population. In the nineteen-thirties – that is, the period between the wars – it is perfectly true to say that British agriculture was in a very depressed condition. At that time we were producing only between 30 and 35 per cent of the food consumed. In other words, two-thirds of what we ate was being imported. The advent of the war brought virtually siege conditions. Not only was shipping very badly needed for other purposes, but the danger and difficulty of bringing food to this country were of course enormous. We could have been blockaded to such an extent that we could have been starved out. Our agricultural industry was ready for the emergency; it had been prepared for it for some time before, and with the outbreak of war our new agricultural machine was jammed straight into top gear. Within quite a short time our whole farming economy had been changed. Instead of a reliance of stock-farmers and milk producers on imported feeding stuffs they were growing their own. We embarked upon a great wartime plough-up campaign. Ploughed land is not only more productive than grassland, it is also more flexible. Human beings cannot eat grass, but human beings can eat all the cereals, they can, if need be, survive on the turnips and potatoes grown on ploughland normally for feeding to animals. At the present time there is obviously a contrast between long-term and short-term views of agriculture. The short-term view is why bother to preserve agricultural land, why bother to produce our own food if we can purchase more cheaply from abroad as a result of the sale of our manufactured goods? That was the old policy. The question is: are we sure we shall never again face the possibility of siege conditions, of having to live on our own humps? Even if we do not require immediately the production of agricultural commodities in this country, for heaven's sake let us not destroy the possibility of so doing in case of dire necessity. In other words, let us not build on the best agricultural land which is capable of producing the food to maintain our population. We can in so many cases use land for industrial and housing purposes which is much less fertile, we must keep the reserve if and when required – that is the long-term point of view.

With the very varied physical conditions which exist in Britain, with its large extent of upland, moorland, land above 1,000 feet with a very heavy rainfall, by no means all parts of the country are suitable for farming. The rough grazing which occupies two-thirds of Scotland, one-third of Wales, and something like 10 per cent of England is mainly in that form because it is not suitable for more intensive production as enclosed arable or grassland. Though much of such hill-land could be made more productive, as the great work of Sir George Stapledon on the improvement of hill pastures has shown, a large part is more productive under forest – hence the need for integration between farming and forestry. Into the same picture must be fitted sporting interests and public access.

To sum up the points of view put forward in this chapter, the most important conclusion is that there is great need for integration between essential uses of land. Rival claimants are each very apt to regard their particular requirement of land as being the most important. The whole question in a crowded country like Britain is to balance the various interests. In so doing there are three golden rules to be observed. The first may be called the rule of optimum use. It is the attempt, and often it cannot be more than an honest endeavour, to determine what is the optimum, or the optimal, use of any given piece of land in the national interest. This can be a national problem where large tracts are concerned; it is also essentially a local problem which enters into the sphere of every town-planning authority in Britain. For any given piece of land it is possible to say that

there is a use for it which is not only of great importance at
the present time, but also of the greatest importance when
the future is considered. The essence of town planning is the
attempt to find this optimum use.

The second principle is the principle of the multiple use,
or multiple-purpose use of land, whereby the same piece of
land can serve more than one purpose. Some of the great
moorlands of this country are valuable as pastures for hill
sheep, valuable as gathering-grounds for water supply for
the neighbouring towns, valuable for the facilities they offer
for air and exercise for those who are energetic enough to
seek the footpaths by which they are traversed – three uses
at least. Similarly, if such land is forested there is a production of timber, again a gathering ground, and again the
possibility of public access. Some of the same land may
serve in the conservation of nature; other parts may be used
for sporting purposes. On a smaller scale the question of
multiple use arises in towns in the varied use of parks.

The third rule is that in a country such as Britain there
ought not to be any waste land; there should be no land
which is not serving some purpose useful to the community.
In the past there has been an aftermath of waste from
mineral working – large tracts of land left derelict and
virtually useless. Great stretches of land from which gravel
and clay have been removed have been left as waterlogged
wastes – a state of affairs we discuss in Chapter 9 as wholly
unjustified.

In the allocation of our scarce resources of land for the
varied requirements of our people, economic considerations
are not the only ones. We have an incalculably valuable
heritage from the past in all that makes up the countryside –
not only the ancient churches and monuments of a similar
character which are well known, but the beauty of the old
English or Welsh quiet countryside. In so many cases it is
the sum total of what we have which is so important, and
which we wish to try to conserve. The pattern of the countryside which has grown up in the course of time, with its fields
and its hedgerows, its winding lanes, its gardens, its pictur-

esque buildings, is important to the country not only because of its aesthetic appeal, but also as the basis of one of our most lucrative sources of wealth, that is to say the tourist industry. It would be utterly wrong to imagine that those who are so concerned with preserving the countryside – a function well understood by the Council for the Preservation of Rural England and the Council for the Preservation of Rural Wales – are thinking purely in terms of sentimental aesthetics. We have in our hands a solid capital asset of great value, but one easily destroyed by careless 'development'.

Our present system of town and country planning does not give a complete answer. When one is up against aesthetic standards questions of individual and public taste come very much into the picture. The problem has become more acute in recent years owing to the standardization of materials, the extensive use of cement in paving-stones and artificially straight kerbstones, the ghastly standard designs of concrete lamp-posts now found everywhere. It is indeed within the last few years that the word 'Subtopia' was created in a famous article in the *Architectural Review* which referred to the spread, as it were of a rash, all over the country of half-baked urban concepts. Unfortunately it is still going on, and will do so until a greater degree of public interest is aroused.

CHAPTER 8

The Classification of Land

IN the preceding chapter we have indicated some of the competing claimants to land. For some purposes it is the situation or other factors rather than the character or quality of the land which matters. Provided there is good access, with agriculture it is essentially the type and potential productivity of the land which matters both in the first instance and in long-term planning. There is a consequent need for some system of land classification.

The British Government, when it declared that, other things being equal, the conservation of good agricultural land would henceforward be national policy, found itself in a quandary. No definition existed of 'good agricultural land', and certainly no attempt had been made to map the distribution of land of differing qualities in Britain. The Geological Survey, when it was established in the forties of last century, had been charged with the study not only of the country's mineral resources, but also of its soils. Apart from some scattered pioneer investigations of soil texture, the latter part of its function had been completely ignored, or at least deferred for future consideration. After much negotiation a Soil Survey under the late Professor G. W. Robinson was set up shortly before the Second World War, but was prevented by the outbreak of that war from getting seriously into its stride.

When, under the shadow of Napoleon's threatened invasion, the Government of George III set up the 'Board of Agriculture and Internal Improvement' as an independent body in 1793, one of the first acts of the Board was to commission a series of County Reports on the state of agriculture. Many of these include a map of the soils of the county, named, classified, and described by farmers for farmers. Such terms as 'good loams', 'light loams', 'marshland clay', and 'peat' are self-explanatory and their meaning is obvious enough, but we have tended to forget what 'brashy' soils mean to Midland farmers or 'dunstone' to the Devonian. These early maps are in fact crude maps of soil regions and indicate a classification of land based on soil texture.

Fig. 15. An early attempt to classify land in an English county

Modern pedology or soil science has become a complex study in its own right. It seeks to study soils and their genesis, in the first place at least, as untouched by man, and without direct reference to their use. Whilst most soils derive the bulk of their material from the underlying rocks, and are thus linked in character and distribution with the geological map – the 'drift' map, not the 'solid' map – they owe much to the climatic conditions under which they are formed and the consequent circulation of water and plant growth. When undisturbed in nature they tend to show marked differences from the surface downwards, with the result that distinct 'horizons' are developed in the 'soil profile'. The development of horizons is hindered by man's activities, for ploughing naturally mixes the upper layers down to six or eight or more inches, according to the depth of ploughing. Indeed, agricultural activity such as deep ploughing or 'double spitting' by the gardener is designed deliberately to destroy the horizons which would naturally develop. Thus the soil series which is the unit of the modern pedologist used in soil mapping is not necessarily related directly to utilization, and some critics would urge that the modern soil map is less informative to the farmer or forester than the older soil maps which emphasize primarily texture and soil depth.

It follows that the modern soil map, valuable though it may be, does not furnish the whole answer to the classification of land where other factors must be taken into consideration. In those parts of the world where population is sparse and where Nature appears to have been little disturbed by the activities of man, the natural vegetation forms a good index to the general character of the land. Taken as a whole, however, vegetation can be a deceptive guide. Many of the magnificent coniferous forests of Canada seem to flourish on almost bare rock: there would certainly be no soil fit for ploughing if the forests were cleared. Similarly, the luxuriant growth of tropical, especially equatorial, forests induced a wide belief in the inherent richness of tropical soils which has proved a myth when the forests have been cleared.

In a country long settled such as Britain little 'natural' vegetation survives, but the semi-natural vegetation of the uplands, such as the heath and grass moorlands, affords a good index of the general character of the underlying soil. Skilful land agents and land valuers have long been accustomed to look at the size and shape of estate trees, to note the character of a grass sward, and to rub a little of the soil through their fingers for texture and organic content whilst testing its depth with an auger. These simple tests measure, however, more than the character of the land: they are measuring also the skill or lack of skill in land management, past and present. Similarly, a classification based on crop yields may differentiate between good and bad farmers rather than between good and bad land.

It is not surprising that there is a considerable divergence of point of view on the classification of land.

It is perhaps natural that in America, where much of the land has been settled for only a couple of generations or so and where present use may reflect only folly or a slavish following of custom with disastrous results, the emphasis should be on potential, ignoring present use. There, widely used schemes are into 'Land Capability Classes'. A simple one distinguishes three classes which are based on the local relief, climate, soil, and vegetation – the criteria which a geographer would use in delineating minor natural regions. So far as soil is concerned, attention is paid not so much to the profile and genesis as to structure, texture (especially for holding water and nutrients), and fertility status. The land is then zoned broadly within the three main groups, according to anticipated results of different types of use:

A Land which is cultivable but ranges widely in fertility – capable of carrying various arable crops or grass in rotation or permanent.

B Land which should not be cultivated but is suitable for the poorer grades of permanent pasture (rough grazing) or timber production.

C Land unsuitable for economic use as arable, grazing, or afforestation.

A similar approach was used in the Montana Land-use Survey, where a dozen 'range types', ranging from grassland through brush and forest to absolutely bare ground, were distinguished. A *Range Type* is defined as 'a type of country which because of a certain uniformity of climate, soil, and

vegetation, may be submitted to uniform land use'. A modi-
fication of this scheme was used for the aerial land classification survey commissioned by the Government of Jordan
(published in 1956). On the other hand, a somewhat similar
broad grouping of land types prepared from air photographs
at the order of the Government of Pakistan covering the whole
Indus valley plain was called a 'Soil Reconnaissance' Survey.

In a closely-settled and old-settled country such as
Britain the problem of land classification is more complex,
though there is also a greater wealth of material from which
to draw. At the request of the Royal Commission on the
Geographical Location of the Industrial Population (the
Barlow Commission), I undertook in 1938 to use all the
varied information collected in the course of the work of the
Land Utilisation Survey to draw up a classification of land
suitable for a broad national policy of land-use planning
and conservation of land resources. It was clear that a
classification into *types* of land was needed, since what is the
'best' land for one purpose is not necessarily the best for
another. Indeed, the conditions for the growing and ripening of cereal crops – wheat, barley, and oats – are not only
different according to the cereal concerned, but markedly
different from the conditions needed for the luxuriant
growth of fodder crops. Ten types of land suggested themselves, and expert opinion on tentative suggestions was
widely sought and freely given. At a later stage a group of
soil surveyors favouring a simple good, medium, and poor
classification joined in a two-day conference to thrash out an
agreed compromise. The story is told in detail in my book
The Land of Britain: Its Use and Misuse. The map showing
the ten types and their distribution over England, Wales,
and Scotland was published on the scale of 1 : 625,000
(roughly 10 miles to the inch) by the Ordnance Survey in
two sheets for the National Planning Series of the Ministry
of Town and Country Planning. The classification, with
shortened definitions, is given below: the letters A, G, and H
indicate a general suitability for arable, grassland, and
heath or rough grazing respectively.

The Classification of Land

MAJOR CATEGORY I – *Good-quality Land*

Highly productive when under good management. Land in this category has the following characteristics:

Site 1 not too elevated
Site 2 level, gently sloping, or undulating
Site 3 favourable aspect
Soil 1 deep
Soil 2 favourable water conditions (actual or potential)
Soil 3 texture, mostly loams but including some peats, sands, silts, and clays

The three criteria under Site apply to all the four types of good agricultural land:

1. *First-class Land capable of intensive cultivation*, especially of foodstuffs for direct human consumption. The soils are deep, and in texture are mainly loams, but include some peats, fine sands, silts, and loamy clays. Drainage must be free, but not excessive, and the soils must not be excessively stony, and must work easily at all seasons.

2. *Good General-purpose Farmland.* This land is similar to the first, but is marred by (*a*) less depth of soil, or (*b*) presence of stones, or (*c*) occasional liability to drought or wetness, or (*d*) some limitation of seasons when the soil works easily, resulting in a restriction of the range of usefulness. When the conditions are such that the land is particularly suitable for arable cultivation the designation 2(A) may be used; when the conditions are such – notably in wetter regions – that sown grasses or permanent grassland are particularly suitable the designation 2(AG) may be used, and such land has been shown by a separate colour on the map.

3. *First-class Land with water conditions especially favouring grass.* This land is similar to 1, but as a result of (*a*) a high permanent water-table, or (*b*) liability to winter or occasional flooding, or (*c*) somewhat heavier or less tractable soils, it is unsuitable or less suitable for arable cultivation

than for grass. Such land may often be converted into Category 1 by drainage or prevention of flooding, but this is a major operation.

4. *Good but Heavy Land.* Although such land has soils of good depth and the natural fertility is often high, the soils are heavy – mostly of the better clays and heavy loams – with the result that both the period of working and the range of possible crops are restricted. Because of these difficulties most of this land in England, though not in Scotland, was down to grass before the Second World War. Some would place such land in the category of medium-quality land, yet for certain crops such land is the finest of all. In England, because of the predominance of grass, the designation 4(G) may be used, but 4(A) would be more appropriate on the boulder clays of Scotland.

MAJOR CATEGORY II – *Medium-quality Land*

This is land of only medium productivity even when under good management. Productivity is limited by reason of the unfavourable operation of one or more of the factors of site or soil character, e.g. by reason of:

Site 1 high elevation
Site 2 steepness
Site 3 unfavourable aspect
Soil 1 shallowness
Soil 2 defective water conditions

It is obvious that a wide range of conditions – indeed an almost endless combination of one, two, or more deleterious factors – is included in this major category. The Land Utilisation Survey recognized that the two chief types of harmful conditions were (*a*) soil and (*b*) relief, and though a wide range is possible within each, this gives Categories 5 and 6.

5. *Medium-quality Light Land.* This is land defective by reason of lightness and, usually, shallowness of soil. The moderate elevation, relatively gentle slopes, and consequent

Good Quality Land ■
Good Quality Land mixed with poorer quality land ⋯

0   Scale of Miles   100

Fig. 16. The distribution of the better farm lands of England and Wales

aspects are all satisfactory. There are several distinct types included within the category, the chief being:

   a. shallow light soils on chalk or Jurassic limestones – the downland and Cotswold soils where ploughable 5(A); where not ploughable 5(G).

b. shallow soils on some of the older limestones and shallow light soils which occasionally occur on other older rocks – usually not ploughable owing to rock outcrops, hence 5(G).

c. light soils, including gravels, not necessarily shallow, which occur on solid formations such as the Bunter Sandstone of Sherwood Forest or on superficial deposits as in Breckland or on consolidated sand-dune areas as in some of the coastal districts of Scotland. Such land is usually best managed as ploughland, hence 5(A).

6. *Medium-quality General Purpose Farmland.* This is land defective primarily by reason of relief – land broken up by steep slopes, with patches of considerable elevation, varied aspect, and varied water conditions. In consequence, soils are varied, often deficient by reason of stoniness, shallowness, heaviness, or in other ways. When a tract of country of this general character is studied in detail it is usually possible to resolve it into a mosaic of small tracts or patches; it may be only a part of a field in size, of land varying from Categories 1 to 10. Most land of Category 6 usually favours a mixture of crops and grass, hence the designation 6(AG).

MAJOR CATEGORY III – *Poor-quality Land*

Land of low productivity by the extreme operation of one or more factors of site and soil.

a. extreme heaviness and/or wetness of soil, giving poor quality heavy land or land in need of extensive drainage works

b. extreme elevation and/or ruggedness and/or shallowness of soil, giving mountain moorland conditions

c. extreme lightness of soil with attendant drought and poverty, giving poor quality light land

d. several factors combining to such an extent as to render the land agriculturally useless or almost so – such as shingle beaches or moving sand dunes

7. *Poor-quality Heavy Land.* This includes the more intractable clay lands and low-lying areas needing extensive

drainage works before they can be rendered agriculturally useful. For convenience, undrained mosses have been included, though the soils they might eventually yield would not necessarily be heavy. The heavy clay lands tend to be in grass, hence the designation 7(G).

8. *Poor-quality Mountain and Moorland.* The wide variety of land included in this category is apparent from the varied character of the natural or semi-natural vegetation by which it is clothed.

9. *Poor-quality Light Land.* This category includes the so-called 'hungry' or overdrained lands, usually overlying coarse sands or porous gravels and hence including both coastal sand dunes and the inland sandy 'wastes' or heathlands.

10. *Poorest Land.* In its present state this land may be agriculturally useless, but this is not to deny possibilities of reclamation. Salt marshes can be drained, sand dunes fixed, and so on.

Some idea of the extent of each type is to be gained from the following table, but the good lands are, as shown in Fig. 16, far from being evenly distributed over the country. The best lands, Types 1 and 3, are both restricted in area and sharply localized – some in areas very vulnerable to urban expansion, as in Lancashire and Kent.

This classification is obviously broad and general. The areas covered by each type were marked out broadly in pencil on the Land Utilization maps on the scale of 1 inch to 1 mile, and these formed the basis for the small-scale map. It is not a permissible procedure to enlarge the latter up to a detailed scale required for a town plan. But the scheme can be applied, with local subdivisions if needed, for a special survey on a large scale. Such surveys were in fact carried out for the Plymouth Plan and published on the 1-inch scale, for the Greater London Plan, and published on the $\frac{1}{4}$-inch scale, for the Liverpool Plan (with greater detail), for the Hull Plan, and others.

It would be idle to pretend that this simple tenfold classification of the land of Britain is the final answer to the problem.

CLASSIFICATION OF LAND IN BRITAIN

	England and Wales		Scotland		Great Britain	
	Acres	Per cent	Acres	Per cent	Acres	Per cent
CATEGORY I – GOOD	17,845,900	47.9	3,963,300	20.8	21,809,200	38.7
1 First Class	1,963,100	5.3	396,800	2.1	2,359,900	4.2
2 Good General farmland						
2(A) for ploughing	7,065,600	18.9	1,735,900	9.1	8,801,500	15.6
2(AG) crops or grass	2,636,900	7.1	192,900	1.0	2,829,800	5.0
3 First Class, restricted	1,234,800	3.3	8,700	0.0	1,243,500	2.1
4 Good but heavy	4,945,500	13.3	1,629,000	8.6	6,574,500	11.7
CATEGORY II – MEDIUM	11,933,800	32.0	2,877,400	15.1	14,811,200	26.3
5 Medium light land						
5(A) for ploughing	2,402,100	6.4	77,400	0.4	2,479,500	4.4
5(G) not for ploughing	220,100	0.6	300	0.0	220,600	0.4
6 Medium general farmland	9,311,400	25.0	2,779,700	14.7	12,111,100	21.5
CATEGORY III – POOR	6,350,900	17.0	12,113,800	63.5	18,464,700	32.8
7 Heavy land	825,900	2.2	54,100	0.3	880,000	1.6
8 Mountain and moor	4,516,800	12.1	12,001,700	62.9	16,518,500	29.3
9 Light land	811,800	2.2	57,900	0.3	869,700	1.5
10 Poorest land	196,400	0.5	100	0.0	196,500	0.4
Closely built over	1,142,700	3.1	114,200	0.6	1,256,900	2.2
TOTAL	37,273,300		19,068,700		56,342,000	

As the Soil Surveys of England and Wales and of Scotland continue with their detailed mapping of soils, working mainly on the scale of $2\frac{1}{2}$ inches to the mile and publishing on the 1-inch scale, it should prove possible to evaluate each of the soil series mapped, though this is not a primary object of the survey. Even so, there is the problem of the man-made soil or of land on which so much skill and money have been expended that it stands apart from neighbouring land once identical. A noteworthy case is with the making of allotments and market gardens tended over the years with loving care.

A major problem remains. What is the relative productive capacity of the various types? Officially some notice has been taken of this problem. In the 1941 Farm Survey conducted by the Ministry of Agriculture 10 acres of rough grazing (normally developed on land of types 8 and 9) were regarded as equivalent in productive capacity to 1 acre of improved farmland – say of types 2 and 4. Following on this general idea, I introduced the concept of a 'Potential Production Unit' * as a standard, and a very rough equation is as follows:

$$
\begin{array}{ll}
\text{One acre of types 1 and 3} & = \text{2 P.P.U.} \\
\text{One acre of types 2 and 4} & = \text{1 P.P.U.} \\
\text{One acre of types 5 and 6} & = \text{0·5 P.P.U.} \\
\text{One acre of types 7, 8, and 9} & = \text{0·1 P.P.U.}
\end{array}
$$

* A Potential Production Unit may be defined as the potential production of one acre of good average farmland under good management. It is not intended to be a fixed or absolute unit, hence the insertion of 'potential'. It is intended to be used to help in comparing the potential production of land of different types. If there were an overall increase in farming output and yields consequent upon technological progress, the *actual* output per acre would increase but the potential of one type of land compared with another might remain relatively the same. There is nothing essentially new in such a concept. A pound is equal to twenty shillings, but the purchasing power or equivalent in goods may change. Land values are influenced by many factors: otherwise one might expect, other things being equal, the value of agricultural land to show a reasonable relationship to ranking in terms of PPU. By way of contrast the Standard Nutrition Unit, discussed later, is an absolute unit.

Using these figures and applying them to the table given above one gets:

		Total for England and Wales mn. units
I GOOD LANDS		
Type 1 one acre = 2 P.P.U.		3·9
,, 2 one acre = 1 P.P.U.		9·7
,, 3 one acre = 2 P.P.U.		2·5
,, 4 one acre = 1 P.P.U.		4·9
II MEDIUM LANDS		
Type 5 one acre = 0·5 P.P.U.		1·3
,, 6 one acre = 0·5 P.P.U.		4·7
III POOR LANDS		
Type 7 one acre = 0·1 P.P.U.		0·1
,, 8 one acre = 0·1 P.P.U.		0·5
,, 9 one acre = 0·1 P.P.U.		0·1
,, 10 one acre =	—	—
		27·7 mn. units

Thus, in total, the 37,273,300 acres of England and Wales give a total of 27,700,000 P.P.U. Though the poor-quality lands, mainly hill moorlands, cover 12 per cent of the surface, they are only equivalent to 2·3 per cent of potential production.

A possible use for such a scheme is to measure the loss to the nation consequent upon different types of land being used for constructional development. Let us suppose that an expanding town proposes to set aside 500 acres for an industrial estate. If this is taken from average good farmland the nation loses 500 P.P.U. If it is taken from the best land of types 1 or 3 the loss is 1,000 Units, but if from poor sandy land of type 9 the loss to the nation is only 50 Units.

But the measurement of potential production is extraordinarily difficult. It is, indeed, difficult enough to compare actual yields, not only because of the variety of crops, but still more because of the extensive use of land for grass and fodder from which the production of food is indirect – through animal products. Some years ago Professor M. G. Kendall attempted to compare the crop productivity among the counties of England by studying mathematically the yields of ten widely grown crops. His ranking of the counties confirmed in general the assessment of land types – at the top were the Isle of Ely and the Holland District of Lincolnshire, towards the bottom were Cumberland and Westmorland. But there were anomalies. As grass was ignored, the then rich grazing county – the figures were pre-war – of Leicestershire showed up very badly near the bottom.

The primary object of the consumption of food is to supply the body with energy, and this is measured in calories. The daily requirement of calories varies directly with the body surface, and there is a basic requirement to keep the body alive. The requirement goes up with movement and work, to high levels with heavy manual work. This is shown in the following table:

MAN:	Sedentary occupation	2,500 calories per day
	Very active	4,250 ,, ,,
WOMAN:	Sedentary	2,100
	Very active	3,750
	Lactation	3,000
CHILD:	Under one year	800
	1–6 years	1,450
	7–12 years	2,200
BOY:	13–15 years	3,150
GIRL:	13–15 years	2,750

(From *Manual of Nutrition*, H.M.S.O.)

Averaging these and other figures, which apply to our conditions in Britain, the daily requirement is 2,460 calories. This is equivalent to 900,000 calories a year, and I have ventured to call this a Standard Nutrition Unit. Some of the food actually produced by the farmer is wasted in preparation and cooking as well as food thrown away unconsumed, and we may equate this with 1 million calories per annum of food produced by the farmer. It may be urged that the S.N.U. considers *only* energy. But if the diet is sufficiently and wisely varied, the intake of protein, minerals, and vitamins will be adequate, provided the intake of calories is adequate.

By thinking in terms of calorie production we have a measure of land productivity under different crops, including grass supporting livestock, and under different types of farm management.

Let us look first at one or two standard food crops – for example, wheat. The position with regard to wheat is that it takes about eleven bushels, harvested, to produce the million calories, or 900,000 calories for actual consumption. Thus we may say that relying on wheat alone eleven bushels satisfies the needs for one person. Taking the conditions, for example, in Britain, where we have a high yield, a yield of thirty-three bushels per acre would mean that on wheat alone three persons could be supported per acre, or for the yield which is not at all uncommon here of forty-four bushels per acre, one acre would support four persons. We can look upon this as the carrying capacity of the land in terms of persons, provided in this case they are dependent on one particular food.

There are certain countries which have to look primarily to the calorie output of their crops as a means for their continued existence. The supreme example of this is Japan, and the Japanese Government is compelled to encourage quite deliberately the production of high-calorie foods which have also a high yield. That is the reason for the concentration of Japanese production on rice wherever rice is possible and on sweet potatoes on types of land where rice or wheat production is impossible. They cannot afford to allow land to be used for the extravagant purposes of keeping cattle for meat or sheep for meat and wool, or even of keeping cattle for milk. Because of the extremely high yields of Japanese ricefields which are consequent upon the careful selection of seed, the intensive use of manure, particularly human manure, hand cultivation, and the use of every tiny fragment of land, we get the fantastic position that with double and treble cropping some of the rice-lands of Japan support as many as six or seven persons per acre. In the case of Japan it does mean that the intake of protein either has to be from a limited amount of vegetable protein, obtained particularly from beans, or that there must be a search for protein from other sources, particularly from a very large consumption of fish. Turning to conditions in Britain, with the varied diet to which we are accustomed and our high standard of living, it requires a very much larger amount of land to produce one Standard Nutrition Unit. The very interesting calculations which have been made by Mr James Wyllie, formerly of Wye Agricultural College in the University of London, show that in certain of the pre-war years it required 1·86 acres to produce the food required for one human being, and that under the strenuous conditions of wartime this figure was reduced to 1·15 acre. We can readily turn this into terms of Standard Nutrition Units and say that our average, when the land is being really well farmed, is an output something in the order of between 800,000 and 850,000 calories per acre. It ought to be explained that this is acreage of *improved* farmland, that is to say crops and managed or enclosed grass. Wyllie ignores rough grazing or rough land as insufficiently important to affect the results. He was thus measuring the average productive capacity of all British land used and improved by farmers, some of it very good, some good, some medium quality, some only poor or marginal. It should be noted that in the years before the Second World War, Britain imported the bulk of her cereal requirements, and specialized in the production of milk, meat, and eggs, based on grassland management rather than on ploughland. During the war the concentration was on ploughland, and the growing of high-calorie cereals, including a considerable proportion of wheat, and potatoes. The post-war period has seen a partial return to the emphasis on milk, meat, and eggs, for various reasons. The climatic conditions in this country are not primarily suitable for the production of wheat, and the type of wheat we produce is not the best for the making of bread. On the other hand, our overseas suppliers have ideal conditions for the production of wheat, and wheat is a commodity which can be easily stored, handled, and shipped, whereas the same is by no means true of things like fresh vegetables, meat, and eggs.

Because of the wartime concentration on high-calorie crops instead of meat it took much less land to produce one Standard Nutrition Unit. But British people are not content to exist on bread and potatoes, and they demand a wide range of meat, milk, vegetables, and fruit. Meat production is particularly extravagant in the use of land. Taking the 1953 figures, out of a total area of 31,176,767 acres in crops and grass, only just over 6 million acres were used for food for direct human consumption. The remainder was used for supporting animals. If we make due allowance for imported feeding-stuffs, we can say that very roughly it takes about $2\frac{1}{2}$ acres of improved farm land to support each stock unit – that is to say, a fully-grown bullock or a cow in milk or seven sheep. On this basis if we take the average dairy cow in this country as one producing 600 gallons of milk, or 4,800 lb. per year, then we find that the output of calories in dairy-farming is only some 576,000 per acre. In other words, it requires $1\frac{3}{4}$ acres roughly to yield one Standard Nutrition Unit in milk. The potential production as far as calories is concerned is thus only one-fifth of that possible with the same-quality land under wheat. Of course milk is a highly protective and almost perfect food, but we must remember that it is one very extravagant of land. Summarizing the British position, if one takes the mixed-farming characteristic of the country, it may be said that with a really good standard of farming, one acre of improved land can be made to produce one Standard Nutrition Unit of a million calories to support one person. This is much reduced if there is a swing to meat and milk; it can be considerably increased if the swing is to cereals or potatoes. It must also be linked with the quality of land. It can be doubled on the highest-quality land. It must be halved if one is thinking of medium-quality land, whereas if one thinks in terms of using the poor hill land probably something like five to ten times the acreage is actually required. In other words, we come back again to the importance of determining our inherently good land and of conserving it, if not for our needs at the moment, at least for the future of our country.

To some extent the figures given in the preceding paragraph are out of date, because of the New Agricultural Revolution noted on page 64; but the principle remains the same.

CHAPTER 9

The Evolution of Town and Country Planning in Britain

THAT eminent jurist, the late Lord Justice Scott, once said that 'town planning is the art of which geography is the science'. His judicial mind was seeing clearly the influence of geographical factors in all that the physical planner would wish to do, and no apology is therefore required for including this chapter on the evolution of town and country planning in Britain.

National planning on a grand scale was practised here nearly 2,000 years ago by the Romans. They were masters of the urban life: their concept was one of well-placed cities where the gracious Roman way of life could be followed within protecting walls, linked by ruler-straight highways well paved and maintained. The frontiers were guarded by strategically placed fortress towns: particularly dangerous frontiers, such as that with the ever-turbulent people of Scotland, were demarcated by a defensible wall. The countryside could be left to the natives, except where Romans with a taste for country life chose to establish their mansions (*villae*) and farm estates. The Romans had no illusions about the climate of Britain: their system of central heating by hot air has scarcely been surpassed to the present day. The Romans established control over the whole area corresponding closely with Lowland Britain, leaving Highland Britain or the Celtic fringe to look after itself. Whether they selected existing settlements for elevation to city status or chose new sites, they worked with a consummate understanding of site factors. Only two of their chosen sites have failed to survive to this day as important cities: conversely, few of the major cities of lowland Britain, except for those dependent on the development of coal resources during the Industrial Revolution, are without a Roman foundation.

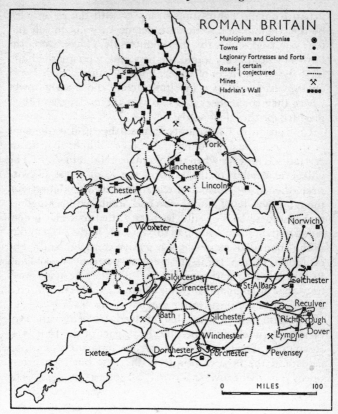

ROMAN BRITAIN

Municipium and Coloniae
Towns
Legionary Fortresses and Forts
Roads { certain
{ conjectured
Mines
Hadrian's Wall

York
Manchester
Chester
Lincoln
Wroxeter
Norwich
Gloucester
Cirencester
St. Albans
Colchester
Reculver
Bath
Silchester
Richborough
Winchester
Lympne
Dover
Exeter
Dorchester
Porchester
Pevensey

0   MILES   100

Fig. 17. The Romans' National Plan for Britain

We think automatically of Carlisle, Newcastle, Manchester, York, Bath, Exeter, Winchester, Chichester, Colchester, Canterbury, Dover, and, of course, London itself. Uriconium shifted later to become Shrewsbury; only Silchester died.

Any road map of Britain reveals the Roman roads. They are straight: most have survived to become the main motor roads of today. They are the hallmark of the tidy-minded urban Romans, contrasting strangely with the records left by the Anglo-Saxon settlers who came later not to rule but to tame and cultivate the countryside. They were the farmers who quickly found the best soils, who guarded and used the best sources of water, but who turned their backs on the roads and saw in cities merely the market towns where they could meet and carry on the exchange of their produce for their few needs.

Conversion to Christianity focused the rural settlements of the Anglo-Saxons round the village church, soon to be crystallized for ever when the Normans rebuilt in stone. The village leadership of the Lord of the Manor was likewise strengthened by Norman integration into a feudal system, though it was King Alfred who had organized his kingdom into counties. As the centuries passed, the manorial system faded with land enclosure, to survive only to the present day in the anomalous existence of extensive common lands. The evolution of the rural–agricultural pattern of Lowland Britain is a long and complex one: it differs in many ways from that of Highland Britain, where Celtic peoples offered a number of contrasts to the Anglo-Saxons.

The land pattern which had evolved slowly over the centuries was rudely disturbed by the impact of the Industrial Revolution. For two centuries the development of the coal-fields and the flow of people to the new but soon grimy towns on them overshadowed all other changes. The twentieth-century swing over to easily transmitted electric power has emancipated industrial development to a considerable extent from its close spatial association with the coalfields, so that the urban–industrial pattern has spread more widely than before over the older pattern of the countryside.

Official census figures of 'urban' and 'rural' population in Britain show only that rather over 80 per cent of the people live in officially constituted cities, county boroughs, boroughs, and 'urban districts'. But rural districts can and do include many towns of considerable size, some fully industrial, and it is nearer the truth to say that nine-tenths of

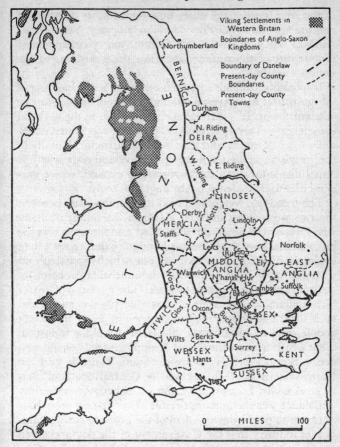

Fig. 18. The Anglo-Saxon settlement

our people live in towns, only one-tenth in villages, hamlets, and the scattered farms and dwellings of the real country-side.

In other words, the electorate, local or national, is 90 per cent urban, and to that extent urban-minded. Only one-tenth knows from birth and daily experience the problems

123

of the countryside; the other nine-tenths must try to learn and understand as one does a foreign language. Yet the one-tenth of our people who live in the country occupy some nine-tenths of the surface: they are the guardians of the national estate.

It would be difficult to pretend that the hasty building of the industrial age gave us automatically either pleasant or efficient towns. It is scarcely surprising that, as the national conscience was aroused, physical planning was at first essentially town planning and that it should arise incidentally to the provision of better housing. The countryside was just something into which the towns might expand, where garden cities and garden suburbs might be built.

The trend of development in Britain in the years between the two world wars induced alarm in the minds of many who foresaw the obvious results. First and foremost was the phenomenal growth of Greater London to the largest urban agglomeration in the world, yet one which sprawled and scattered itself so as to produce innumerable problems of transport and the journey to work. The spread of Greater Birmingham was another comparable phenomenon, and both these magnets seemed to be drawing away the young people, and so sapping the life from the older industrial areas which became the foci of unemployment, despair, and decay. South Wales, West Cumberland, Tyneside and the North-eastern Coalfield, as well as Central Scotland, languished whilst London grew and flourished. An unhealthy unbalance was the apparent result of *laissez-faire* growth.

It was to probe this problem of the growing maldistribution of industry that the Government of the day appointed the Royal Commission on the Geographical Location of the Industrial Population under the Chairmanship of Sir Montague Barlow. The Barlow Commission had not completed its work when war broke out, and, when issued, its Report proved to be a long and complex document divided into a majority report and a minority report. But, in general terms, its trend was obvious. It called for positive Government action – national planning – to secure a more even spread of industry over the country which would resuscitate the older industrial areas and prevent, or at least modify, the continued unwieldy spread of Greater London and Greater Birmingham. In so far as it advocated a planned dispersal of industry, the threat of Hitler's bombs accomplished in a brief span of time what might have been discussed for years without action. Wartime factories grew up all over the country, often in remotest areas, regardless of such economic considerations as accessibility and transport costs, of paramount importance in peacetime.

The inter-war urban sprawl, the proposals of the Barlow Commission, and the actual dispersal of industry consequent upon wartime conditions, all combined to constitute, if not a threat to the continued existence of rural Britain, at least a challenge in adjustment between town and country. The Government in 1941 set up the interdepartmental Committee on Land Utilization in Rural Areas under the Chairmanship of Lord Justice Scott, which was required, under its terms of reference, to 'consider the conditions which should govern building and other constructional development in country areas consistent with the maintenance of agriculture ... having regard to ... the well-being of rural communities and the preservation of rural amenities'.

The Committee worked hard and with dispatch: its best-selling report, issued in August 1942, was destined to be used as the rough blue-print from which a stream of legislation has followed. The main report traces first the genesis and character of the problem and then goes on to a wide range of recommendations. The Government proceeded almost immediately to set up a Ministry of Town and Country Planning – not, it is true, along the lines advocated in the report with overall powers of review, but as a departmental ministry – and the basal recommendations of the Scott Report were embodied in the Town and Country Planning Act of 1947 and the Agriculture Act of 1947. The Scott Committee was relieved of considering the financial aspects of planning because the Government had appointed the Expert Committee on Compensation and Betterment, under the chairmanship of Mr Justice Uthwatt (the Uthwatt Committee), to deal with those problems. The Town and Country Planning Act was thus based on the Government's study of the three Reports. Other major recommendations of the Scott Report, such as the nationalization of the Gas and Electricity industries, were implemented by appropriate separate legislation: other recommendations were made the subject of further investigation. The Scott Committee's recommendations to establish National Parks and Nature Reserves and to survey all footpaths were exhaustively studied, and resulted in due course in the establishment of the National Parks Commission and the demarcation of appropriate parks and of the Nature Conservancy under the National Parks Act of 1949. The survey of footpaths was made part of the work of the County Planning Authorities. The Scott recommendation for the registration of title to land was further considered by the House of Lords Committee on Registration of Title under Lord Rushcliffe's chairmanship. Its unanimous recommendation for registration has had to be postponed in execution for reasons of administrative difficulty.

It was my privilege to serve as Vice-Chairman of the Scott Committee and afterwards on the Footpaths Committee (under the Chairmanship of Sir Arthur Hobhouse) and the Rushcliffe Committee.

Although the Ministry of Town and Country Planning and its successor the Ministry of Housing and Local Government are required to deal with the physical planning of both town and country, and although the County Planning Authorities set up under the 1947 Act must deal with the whole of their areas, there is obvious need for a specialist study and specialist advice in the country's largest industry – that of agriculture. To carry out these studies and to be ready with the appropriate advice, the Ministry of Agriculture and Fisheries (now the Ministry of Agriculture, Fisheries and Food) set up a Central Planning Branch in 1942–3. It was my function as Chief Adviser on Rural Land Use, aided by my ten Rural Land Use Officers (one in each of the Civil Defence Regions covering England and Wales), to deal with the problems of the countryside in the national planning picture. In due course the work so expanded that the Agricultural Land Service was reorganized to deal with the planning aspects of rural land use *vis-à-vis* the other Ministries concerned with use of land and planning. By interdepartmental understanding the Board of Trade is the paramount authority in industrial location, the Ministry of Housing and Local Government on planning aspects, the Ministry of Agriculture, Fisheries and Food on the use of open land required for development.

In practice Britain is now probably more advanced in the planning of its land resources than any other country in the world. The position may be explained thus. Under the Town and Country Planning Act of 1947 planning is compulsory for the whole country, and the county (and County Borough which has the status of a county) has been made the planning unit. Each county is required to prepare (*a*) a factual survey and (*b*) a plan for future development based on the survey. Each county was given up to five years to carry out this work before submitting its results to the Minister. The survey and plan are then examined by Ministry officials, and in this way co-ordination of policy between one region and another can be obtained, and the Minister appoints Inspectors to hold inquiries at which local objections are heard. The plan is then approved as submitted or suitably modified and becomes the basis of development.

There is some difficulty that a series of county plans, however good in themselves, do not make up a national plan, but certain matters are decided on a national basis. The encouragement of industry in the nationally demarcated Development Areas is a good example; the designation of National Parks is another; main trunk roads and new motorways a third. The county plans, which are by instruction designed especially to consider the needs of the immediate future – the next five years in particular – and in relation to the 'foreseeable future' of twenty years, are but outline sketches. Provision is in fact made for revision every five years.

Prior to the 1947 Act planning was voluntary or permissive, not compulsory. The passing of the Act meant the setting up of planning departments in all the counties, and the surveys gave employment to a considerable army, especially of those trained in geographical methods of survey and analysis. The Plan, based on the survey, is the field of work of the professional Town Planner.

This is not the place to detail the work of the town planner in preparing the plans for submission to the Minister under the 1947 Act. Suffice it to say that the plans usually consist of two parts – an outline plan for the county as a whole, and separate plans for the more important towns, on a larger scale and of course with more detail. Although there is this distinction based primarily on administrative areas, there is also another twofold division, which is of more importance perhaps in our present consideration. That is the rather more natural division into town and country. It has already been mentioned that the protection of rural interests, which are primarily, of course, the interests of the farmer, has come to be regarded as the sphere of work of the Ministry of Agriculture, Fisheries and Food. On the other hand, the planning of developments within an actual town is obviously not the concern of this Ministry, but is in the sphere of the professional town planner and his own Ministry – the Ministry of Housing and Local Government. The division between the two, however, by no means generally corresponds with the limits of the administrative divisions. Consequently a very useful working agreement has been reached whereby the Ministry of Agriculture, through the Agricultural Land Service, surveys roughly a town area and draws a line on a map which has come to be called the Urban Fence. This in fact demarcates the effective built-up area associated with the town. The Ministry of Agriculture then declares it is not concerned with the change of use of land within the Urban Fence except in so far as allotments are concerned. In other words, the town planner is therefore left free to make what changes he considers desirable within the Urban Fence. When there is any question of the town expanding and wishing to use land outside the Urban Fence which is still rural and farmed, then the Ministry of Agriculture requires to be consulted. It became clear from the outset of this idea that most towns would be expanding either to re-house their population under better conditions or actually to accommodate more industry and people. The Ministry of Agriculture therefore goes further, and outside the Urban Fence

Fig. 19. Directing urban expansion. (A) Open land of purely amenity significance. (B) Brown areas (see text). (C) Open land so urbanized as to have little value for farming and therefore included within the Urban Fence

lays down certain tracts, which have come to be called Brown Areas. These are the areas into which urban expansion may take place with as little damage to the countryside and the organization of farming as may be possible. Frequently the Brown Areas are numbered 1, 2, 3, 4, and so on, to indicate the preferred order of development from the agricultural point of view.

The work of drawing the Urban Fence and of demarcating the Brown Areas involves the officials of the Ministry in a number of investigations. There is of course first and foremost the assessment of qualities of land. Here it is necessary to take the long-term rather than the short view. The short

view would look at well-farmed pieces of land and regard
them as of prime importance, and would suggest that tracts
of land which are neglected are not of comparable importance. This, however, should give place to the long view
based on potential productivity or the intrinsic qualities of
the land. In many cases the assistance of the Soil Survey of
England and Wales has been enlisted to get the relevant
information on qualities of land around a town.

Another consideration of great importance to agriculture
around towns is the layout of the farms. If a farm is of a
good size, and in one block and well equipped with buildings, it is obviously of value as an economic unit, to be preserved as a whole. If on the other hand, the land is broken
up into small sections separately, cultivated or otherwise
used, it is less important to retain such holdings. Further, it
often happens that around a town agriculture has been rendered difficult or almost impossible by various urban
influences. There is the constant difficulty of trespass, unfortunately in some cases the theft of produce such as vegetables and fruit, but particularly damage by dogs worrying
sheep and even cattle. All these combine to render the
land 'urbanized' and of comparatively little value for agricultural purposes. This is particularly the case if there is a
wedge of agricultural land almost surrounded by housing,
as when an old farm has become engulfed by the natural
spread of the town. It is such urbanized or semi-urbanized
land which is likely to be included by the Agricultural
Officers in their Brown Areas. A very interesting and perhaps rather tricky point arises in connexion with the survey
for the Urban Fence and the Brown Areas. Should the
opinion of the owner or the occupier be sought, should he
be notified of the decision reached by the officers? At first
sight one may say: yes, of course. On the other hand, in
demarcating Brown Areas one is indicating land which may
possibly be used in the future for other purposes. Is it wise
to upset the occupant or owner by telling him of what may
in fact never happen? It is a tricky point, and one very difficult to decide.

In a later chapter we shall have a little more to say about the town planner and the work of his survey team within the bounds of the Urban Fence. What about the open countryside, the area which lies outside the Urban Fence? It is natural that the point of view of the agriculturalist, of

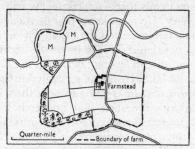

Fig. 20. A well-balanced farm unit

the country dweller, should be somewhat different from that of the town planner looking at the same problems from the overall point of view, but from inside a town. The farmer is concerned, as any industrialist would be, with

Fig. 21. A badly fragmented holding

security of tenure. A manufacturer faced with the possible loss of part of his factory building, such as a few workshops or a main access, would almost certainly say that it was impossible to carry on manufacturing under such conditions. But the farm is also a factory, a carefully balanced unit, and one of the things the farmer needs is security of tenure. A farmer liable to lose a few fields – perhaps his specially valued home meadows – for development, or liable to find his farmstead cut off from his fields by a by-pass or new road, is in an intolerable position. The farmer, especially one concerned with livestock such as a dairy herd, or beef cattle, must plan years in advance – four or five years, at least – to develop his policy. He must know that he is safe to have his land for a much longer period than that. The arable farmer is in the same position if he is to incur the necessarily considerable expenditure in fencing, draining, ditching, liming, and fertilizing his land. He is sinking capital in his land, and he needs to know that he is going to hold the whole. If the physical conditions are such that he needs to farm, for example, on a four-field system or a four-course rotation, he can do that with eight or twelve roughly equal fields, but not with seven or ten. Town planners are apt to forget this when they suggest that taking just one or two fields from a farm can make but little difference. The farmer must have security of tenure. What therefore he needs to know in advance are the possible changes envisaged in the overall plan for the county.

The town-planner's point of view is somewhat different. He is concerned especially with the expansion of towns, but over the land as a whole he is concerned with other matters than simply production of food or raw materials. For example, there is the conservation of beauty, and on county plans are demarcated 'areas of outstanding natural beauty' (AONB). These are perhaps of less significance than the really important tracts of such character which have been made into National Parks. The control as far as possible of buildings and change of use in National Parks will be particularly stringent. Then the town planner from other considerations would normally select certain villages for special purposes – to receive such favours as the development of village colleges and to be made into what have been called 'King' or 'Key Villages' for the countryside. We have mentioned elsewhere the importance of maintaining the village under modern conditions as a viable unit and of

maintaining its population for this reason. It is not as a rule
possible to demarcate the specific pieces of land which are
going to be developed, and so the general tendency is simply
to indicate that certain villages are likely to be chosen for
purposes of expansion, and it is in those that building
would be particularly encouraged. Certain parts of the
county may well be indicated as suitable for the development of new towns, if such are required, or new industrial
areas.

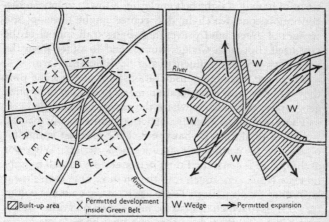

Fig. 22. 'Green Belt' and 'Green Wedge' concepts of town development

Where improvements of communication, especially roads,
are required this is usually indicated on the plan. But the
bulk of the rural countryside will be left on the County
Outline Plans as White Land: agricultural land in which
no particular developments are envisaged. There was a
time when town planners thought considerably about the
actual demarcation of Green Belts. The concept of the
Green Belt has become a somewhat difficult one. A Green
Belt has been looked upon as an area not to be built on, surrounding and bounding towns, preventing their expansion,
and within which there would be much open land available
for recreation, such as golf courses and so on. The more

rational and more modern view of the Green Belt is that it is just part of the ordinary countryside where farming and other rural occupations characteristic of the country are being carried on, but where there will be a deliberate attempt to prevent further construction – in other words, to maintain it as open land, primarily agricultural. But to have a Belt of a definite width around a town would rather naturally cause such a town to jump over the Green Belt and to start expanding beyond it. It would surely be better, instead of having a tight belt enclosing a town, to have a discontinuous one which in due course might develop into wedges of green land preventing the overall sprawl of the city itself. But such wedges would tend to suffer from the proximity of urban influences and be difficult to farm.

These are planning considerations, but at the same time they do bring into consideration many principles of applied geography, particularly where the survey is concerned.

There remain a number of weak points in our overall system of planning. Perhaps one of the weakest is the impossibility of controlling architectural design. Wherever architecture is concerned then personal taste as well as public taste come very much into the picture. One man's meat is another man's poison. There are in many counties voluntary panels to which designs for new houses and other buildings can be submitted, so that one may hope to avoid the worst incongruities in the countryside. But by and large it has proved impossible to control, and probably very undesirable to attempt to control, actual architectural design. Another weakness in our overall planning is comparative lack of control over public authorities: those concerned with water supply, sewerage, electricity supply, and gas supply, as well as the local authorities whose works, admittedly in the public interest, are to a considerable extent outside the machinery of ordinary planning control. But local councils are not always perfect judges of good taste! Buildings which are essentially for agricultural purposes do not require planning consent, but it is not difficult to see that there can be some very atrocious erections in the countryside put up in the name of agriculture, which do far more damage than building of a more urban nature. Changes in the country-side are inevitable, too, with the erection of pylons and, in these days, of atomic power-stations. Effective transmission of radio and television, as well as the protection of the country by a network of radar stations, necessitate the construction of towering masts which have given rise to much controversy.

An interesting point arises with regard to trees. It is possible under the existing legislation, especially in towns, to have tree-preservation orders and prevent the owners from cutting down trees which are regarded as of especial importance from an amenity angle. On the other hand, trees, certainly trees grown together as woodland and forest, must be regarded as a crop, not a crop which is reaped annually, but a crop which in the course of time needs to be thinned, in further time reaches maturity and should be reaped: in other words, the time inevitably comes when a tree is due to be felled. This simple truth is not easily collated with the concept of tree preservation. The important thing is to prevent the spread of derelict land by replanting the areas after felling. We must not look upon trees as if they are something which is permanent. They start from seeds, they grow, they reach maturity, and then comes a stage when decay sets in, and something must be done about it.

Although it would seem at first sight that now we have comprehensive town and country planning over the whole of Britain there is little work for such bodies as the Council for the Preservation of Rural England and the Council for the Preservation of Rural Wales, this actually is far from the truth. These bodies act as watchdogs, and are always on the lookout for acts of vandalism which may be carried out by individuals or corporations, and they should represent the point of view of the citizen anxious to conserve that which is best, and at the same time to encourage natural development and evolution.

We have referred elsewhere to the importance in such a crowded country as ours of avoiding the existence of anything which can be called waste land. This has certainly not been a dominant point of view in the past. There are parts of Britain much disfigured by the tip-heaps of old collieries, by waste from iron ore and other mineral workings, and in fact by industrial waste generally. The old Black Country has long since really ceased to be the smoke-palled Black Country it was in the days when it was the centre of the iron industry of this country. With the exhaustion of the famous Thick Coal and the exhaustion of the local iron ore supplies, the iron industry has moved to other areas, but there has been left, as elsewhere, an aftermath in the form of much derelict land. Fortunately Nature steps in and has clothed many of the old tips with a growth of grass and shrubs but a problem remains. In the Black Country a very careful survey was made, a preliminary one under my direction at the Ministry of Agriculture, and then a much more thorough one under the direction of my colleague, Professor Stanley H. Beaver, now at the University of Keele, North Staffordshire, for the Ministry, as it then was, of Town and Country Planning. The area was surveyed in great detail on a large scale and the old industrial areas and tip-heaps classified into four categories. There were those areas which could be easily levelled and used for playing-fields, housing, and other purposes; there were those which could be levelled at rather greater expense; there was a third category where slopes were too steep and where other use was properly to be sought; and finally, the really hilly tips, old quarries and so on where even modern bulldozing machinery could not be expected to operate. So the treatment proposed ranged from the complete re-use of the more easily reclaimed areas for housing recreation grounds or new industry, to the deliberate creation of 'natural' parks by judicious planting, and the encouragement of what Nature had already done in the hilly areas as seen in the old limestone quarries of Wren's Nest and Castle Hill, Dudley. We see there how a landscape which had been almost ruined by a past industrial epoch can be and in fact is being transformed into one of marked beauty, where the originally rather tame scenery has been varied by the creation of a number of miniature Switzerlands giving great joy to the local inhabitants and providing playing-grounds for the young Robin Hoods or Davy Crocketts of today. But even such derelict areas do not become parks or playgrounds or delectable areas absolutely of their own. Thought must be given to grasses and plants to be encouraged, thought must be given to the type of trees which may be expected to flourish; and so here again we require the knowledge of not only the geographer and the surveyor to make a very careful survey of the area, but also the expert knowledge of the forester, horticulturalist, and the grass expert to come to the rescue and show what can be done with these interesting areas.

In practically every part of the country readers will be familiar with old industrial areas which need to be reclaimed. Some are extremely difficult because of the permeation of the soil by noxious chemicals. We find this in parts of the old smelting areas in South Wales, and in parts of the old saltfields of Cheshire, and so on, but there is tremendous opportunity in the creation of new beauty where such areas are concerned. A very widespread problem is in connexion with ordinary wet-pit gravel workings. Some of them form delightful natural nature reserves in these days, others can be converted with but little effort for boating and bathing. Still others, of course, will require to be filled in so that the land can be re-used. For the infill urban waste is sometimes available, and so occasionally two problems can be solved simultaneously.

The successful planning of land use requires above all cooperation and goodwill among all concerned. Whilst there are now compulsory powers, the best results are rarely obtained by using this big stick. The grant of a licence for surface mineral working is now commonly made conditional on the restoration of the land to serve, if not its original purpose, at least a useful function in the national pattern. This applies to open-cast-coal working and the quarrying of iron ore. Where the seam of coal or of iron ore is at some depth below the surface, and especially where it lies beneath beds of hard rock, the overburden was formerly left to form a rocky desert of 'hill and dale'. Where the nature of the material makes restoration to agricultural use very difficult, some excellent examples of afforestation may be seen. But such restoration of land may be expensive, and the question arises, Who pays? Is it worth while to spend £200 an acre to restore land originally worth only £20? If, however, one remembers that £20,000 worth of mineral may have been taken out of that acre, 1 per cent to keep it a part of the national estate is not excessive.

Very difficult in some areas is the problem of surface subsidence, with consequent interference with drainage, which results from deep mining of such minerals as coal, or the pumping of brine in the saltfields. In due course, when mining has ceased and time has been allowed for subsidence, such areas can be reclaimed for agricultural purposes, but are best avoided by housing and industry. Parts of the country which would otherwise provide good sites for new towns have been eliminated for this reason: in older mining areas the cracked houses, warped floors, and ill-fitting doors and windows are reminders of the troubles due to subsidence, and so too are stagnant meres and reedy fields.

In recent years it has come increasingly to be recognized that between the local plans for counties and major cities on the one hand and the country as a whole on the other, it is necessary to consider the special problems of major regions. The Ministry of Housing and Local Government took the lead in 1964 by publishing an outline plan for the whole of south-east England, facing realistically an estimated population increase of $3\frac{1}{2}$ million in twenty years. Continued population growth both by natural increase and immigration is the major new factor not fully appreciated when the plans of the forties were in preparation.

CHAPTER 10

Photogeography

A STUDY which concerns itself so much with spatial distribution whilst relying primarily on maps and cartograms derives at the same time much help from photographs and from other 'visual aids'. At the instructional level, teachers of geography use photographs and half-tone illustrations not merely as adornments but as a basis for teaching what the printed word fails to convey. A similar technique is used in the planning field. Such pioneer plans for the post-war era as London County, Greater London, Plymouth, Hull, Manchester, and Merseyside were lavishly illustrated with photographs not only attractive in themselves but definitely complementary to the maps and descriptive text of the survey. Photographs are appropriate to a factual objective survey: a skilful photographer makes the best of his subject, but an honest photograph does not lie. Buildings planned for the future cannot be portrayed by actual photographs, and almost inevitably the architect's idealized sketches introduce a subjective note. Of particular value in aiding geographical description are oblique aerial views, but a new and powerful weapon, not as yet fully exploited, has been found in the vertical air photograph.

Studied in stereoscopic pairs, air photos are extraordinarily revealing – so much so that security precautions have led many countries to restrict in one way or another their availability to unofficial investigators. Under the climatic conditions which prevail in many countries it is often difficult to get the clear atmospheric conditions which permit a first-class photograph to be taken, so that prints vary in quality, but it is safe to say that there are very few parts of the earth's surface which have not now been photographed from the air.

Apart from the fact that air photos are just as easily taken of remote areas almost inaccessible by land – such as the heart of tropical forests or remote deserts or trackless swamps – as they are of familiar homelands, they often reveal, even to the untrained observer, features not apparent on the ground itself. To the trained worker the amount of information which can be extracted from a set of air photos is often quite staggering. According to the interest of the student and the technique employed, the same set of photographs may be worked over a dozen times and a dozen different maps produced as a result.

In the first place comes the construction of simple base maps. From air photographs the Directorate of Overseas Surveys is now engaged in mapping the British Colonial areas of Africa and elsewhere, producing a series of un-coloured maps on the scale of 1 : 50,000 or rather more than 1 inch to 1 mile. These, known as 'Preliminary Plots', show rivers, routes, settlements, and the more obvious physical features. Maps on other scales are also being produced.

Elaborate machines now exist with the aid of which much more elaborate maps, fully contoured, can be constructed, and many countries have adopted this as their standard method of survey and map production. This is highly technical and highly specialized work, so that photo-grammetry has become a field of study in its own right. Many universities have professors of photogrammetry, and there is a constant demand for those trained in this work.

We are concerned here more with what may be called a second look at the air photos. The eye of the trained geo-logist can often detect structures – such as fault-lines in forested country – which he might miss even in the most meticulous ground survey. In open desert country the air-photograph may be virtually a ready-made geological map. It is not surprising that the professional photogeologist now exists whose task is to construct provisional geological maps which field parties then take into the field for verification and completion. Most of the great oil companies now work in this way.

Anyone who has flown over desert country will know how the pattern of intensity of scrub vegetation, not apparent on the ground, reveals when seen from the air the presence of underground sources of water. A whole river system with tributaries, meanders, a delta, and so on may exist just underground and stands revealed from the air.

Both in this last case and for the geologist the key is found in the changes in vegetation. Quite remarkably complete maps of the vegetation cover may be constructed: foresters can get such details as the height and density of forests and even estimate timber yields. But why map just forests? The whole picture of the natural and semi-natural vegetation, the use or non-use of the land, the distribution of settlements, and their relationship with areas of cultivation can be seen and mapped. When the Land Utilisation Survey of Britain was carrying out its work in the nineteen-thirties few air photos were available, and the survey was carried out by a field-to-field inspection on the ground, but now, all over the world, land-use surveys are being carried out by air photography. The great Swedish survey, on which national planning of land use is to be based, is actually being carried out by making printed maps from the air photographs on the scale of 1 : 2,500 and over-printing on these in colour the interpretation of land use.

As long ago as the early nineteen-twenties, before stereo-pairs came into use, an aerial survey was carried out of the Irrawaddy Delta Forests in Burma and used as a basis for the carefully planned working of those timber reserves.

In the geographical laboratory of the London School of Economics, under the direction of Mr R. R. Rawson and Mr K. R. Sealy, a complete land-use map of Cyprus was constructed in 1956 from some thousands of maps and then reduced to the scale of 1 inch to 4 miles for publication in one sheet. It is a pioneer-example of what should be done for the whole world.

Similar work is in fact in progress in many parts of the world. Hundreds of thousands of square miles have been mapped in Canada and economic areas of forest delineated.

Work by Miss M. Cunningham in New Brunswick demon-
strated clearly that the cultivated areas were related to
access roads and not to differences in soil or land potential.
Work carried out by Dr A. Irawathy on photographs from
North Borneo showed clearly relative success or failure in
clearing different types of land for rubber or coconuts and
also showed clearly the character of settlement in remote
areas extremely difficult of access.

Not unnaturally the Dutch, who for centuries have been
winning land from the sea and are at present reclaiming the
larger part of the former Zuyder Zee, have a special interest
in the potential value of the land which they are thus gain-
ing. The planning of the land can be carried out right from
the beginning. After the elimination of sea salts, it is very
largely the texture and drainage of the clay, silt, or sand
which determines the necessary treatment with manures,
the management of the soils which will form, and the crops
which will grow. The Dutch have accordingly worked on
methods whereby character of soil can be detected from air
photos. It is certainly the case in some areas of the world at
least that provisional soil maps can be constructed from air
photos. A large-scale pioneer investigation of this sort was
authorized by the Pakistan Government in 1953. Hunting
Aerosurveys were commissioned to take air photos over the
whole of the Indus Plain of Western Pakistan from which
their expert teams were to construct two sets of maps on the
scale of 1 : 250,000 – one set showing existing land use, the
other major soil groups from which potential land use could
be assessed. In this very dry area soils with alkaline or saline
incrustations are difficult to improve, but show up very
clearly in air photos. In other areas any mapping of soils
from air photographs may be much more difficult. In West
Africa for example what may look like marked soil differences are in fact surface phenomena due to the burning of
grass.

Reference has been made to the way in which details of
geological structure difficult to detect on the ground are
often clearly seen in air photos. A still more remarkable case

was revealed by the pioneer work of the late O. G. S. Crawford, author of *Archaeology from the Air*, and Mr E. C. Curwen, since followed by workers in many countries. Outlines of the Celtic fields of 2,000 years ago on the English downlands stand out because of the slight differences, clearly seen in photos, in the strength of growth in grass or crops. Long-forgotten villages, covered with rubble, soil, and even centuries of vegetation growth, can also be detected; the traces of ancient roads and trackways stand out in the same way. The map of Britain is often likened to a palimpsest – the old parchment so valuable that it was used several times over, but where traces of the earlier writing imperfectly removed showed through the latest inscriptions. Often the air photograph is in reality the photograph of a palimpsest. Since the history of land use is so frequently an important guide to its future use in planning, this use of air photography has a significance far beyond its interest to the historian or archaeologist.

CHAPTER II

Some Problems of Climatology

IT would be unfortunate if the impression were left that the only problems in applied geography were related to land and people. Man has his feet on the ground, but his head in the air, and a whole range of problems are proper to the atmosphere in which he lives and which is such an important part of his environment.

Despite opinions which may be held to the contrary, the climate of Britain is not very far from the ideal. So far as temperature is concerned it is never so hot as to prohibit manual work or reduce the body and brain to such a stage of lethargy – by no means unknown in those parts of the tropics which have been called regions of debilitation – that both refuse to work. In winter it is never so cold that one goes out in constant dread of frostbite, yet normally cold enough to encourage health, work, and exercise. In some parts of the country, and in some seasons, rainfall is definitely in excess of needs: on the other hand, failures of crops or water supply by reason of drought are unknown by standards common in many parts of the world. Violent destructive storms, so unpredictable over some of the larger land masses, are practically unknown; even the pea-souper fogs of London have become rarities with the elimination of the smoke and atmospheric pollution on which they so largely depended. We sometimes regret our rather low sunshine records; this in itself is a challenge to make the most of the sunshine we do get, and this is seen in the modern trend towards the extensive use of glass in building.

In a broad way climate limits the growth of all plants. Some cannot stand frost – temperatures below 32°F. or 0°C. – and such tropical plants are not therefore to be found outdoors in Britain. Some plants tolerate frost provided it is not prolonged, and hence some of the distinctive plants of our extreme south-west – on the sheltered coasts of Devon and Cornwall. A crucial temperature in the life of many plants is 42° or 43°F. (6°C.), below which the plant is dormant, above which vegetative growth takes place. Roughly the western half of the main island of Britain has an average temperature in the coldest month of over 40°F. and in the extreme west it is over 43°. This means that grass, for example, is growing throughout the year and affords some grazing right through the winter in western counties. Even in the east animals can usually be left out in the open throughout the year. In the summer the south of Britain is distinctly warmer than the north, so that the hottest month has an average of 63°F. in London, but only 55°F. in the north of Scotland. So the concept of 'accumulated temperatures' has been developed, for example, of day-degrees above 42°. This measure of the sum total of heat available during a season for plant growth is important. The growing season is insufficiently long or the total of accumulated temperature too small over most of Britain for maize (corn) to ripen, and in the north of Scotland may become inadequate for several crops which flourish in the south of England.

Where moisture is concerned there are several crucial figures. A few parts of Britain – around the Thames estuary in particular – have an average rainfall of less than 20 inches a year. With correspondingly good sunshine figures those parts of eastern England and Scotland with less than an average of 30 inches a year have normally conditions conducive to arable farming and the ripening of cereal crops. Where, on the other hand, the rainfall is between 30 and 60 inches, as it is over the greater part of the Midlands and lower ground in the west, conditions are excellent for the growth of grass and fodder crops, with the consequent encouragement of dairy-farming and the fattening of animals. Where, as on the hills of the north and west, the annual total rises to over 60 inches, excess of moisture leading to water-logging and bog conditions and to acidity of soil, combined with the leaching out of plant food, presents a constant problem.

Fig. 23. A simplified rainfall map of the British Isles

These are just some of the broad effects of climate. Snow cover, incidence of fog, exposure to wind are important in some areas, but there is another and much-neglected aspect of climate.

Every gardener knows the contrasts which may exist between his garden and a neighbour's or between one part of

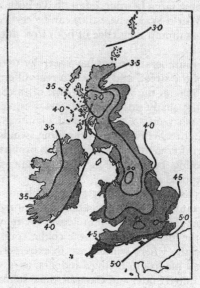

Fig. 24. Sunshine in the British Isles, expressed in average number of hours of bright sunshine per day throughout the year. The maximum possible is twelve hours per day

his own garden and another. He knows well that he cannot grow against a north-facing wall what will flourish with a southerly aspect. In other words, his activities are limited by microclimates.

Microclimatology, or the study of small climates, local climates, though so much neglected, has a most important bearing on land planning. Obviously this is the case for the farmer, but equally it is for the town planner. To take a simple example: cold air tends to behave rather like cold water, to flow downhill, and especially down valleys, and to form a pond or reservoir where it meets an obstruction and piles up. There in winter one finds 'frost pockets', and the lowest temperatures ever recorded in Britain have been in such frost pockets in the Chiltern Hills not far from London. So little, however, is microclimatology studied or understood that some large housing estates have been sited, since the Second World War, where they can be certain of enjoying (?) the maximum incidence of both frost and fog in the winter months.

Although innumerable songs have been written about the sunny side of the street, and there is a real difference in the health of people on the sunny side (*adret* of the Swiss) compared with the shady side (*ubac*) of east–west valleys, little attention is yet paid to this in town planning. Medieval builders sought shelter from prevailing winds: modern builders not infrequently create enormous problems of heating and cooling by employing a maximum of glass for schools in exposed sites.

This leads us to another interesting problem.

An important field of investigation is awaiting the attention of the geographer as a climatologist. We may call it the problem of the ideal climate. In the colder countries of the world, especially where winters are so extremely cold that much of one's life has to be lived indoors, as in the greater part of the United States and Canada, the systematic central heating of buildings has to be undertaken as a matter of course. In fact one creates an artificial climate. Whereas in Britain we regard as a desirable temperature for such institutions as hospitals and schools something of the order of 65° F. in the winter months, the American concept of the ideal climate in this regard is much higher. Europeans are apt to complain bitterly of their early experience of American office buildings which are kept at a temperature between 75° and 80° F. or even higher. This has a bearing on clothing, and the American custom is now to wear the same underclothing, in fact the same clothing, throughout the year. The American businessman is apt to be found working in his shirtsleeves in his office when the temperature outside is below zero.

Since much of the American continent in summer suffers from excessively high temperatures, the air-conditioning or air-cooling of buildings has become very general, and this is spreading to the tropics. The question then is, what temperature should be aimed at, and what humidity? Mistakes were made in the early days of air conditioning, and there were many cases of pneumonia caused by the excessive cooling of buildings when the difference between the temperature outside and the temperature inside was too great. Another trouble was the effect on appetite which has been experienced in the tropics. After a morning in a very hot office one went into an air-conditioned dining-room for lunch, and experiencing the zip caused by the difference in temperature one was tempted to swallow a couple of cocktails, perhaps have a pint of beer with lunch, and thoroughly enjoy one's food in the cool atmosphere, only to find that when one emerged outside afterwards there was a virtually complete collapse owing to the high temperature. It has now been realized that one secret of air conditioning is that the contrasts must not be too great.

An important fact which is not yet fully realized is that it is much cheaper to lower the temperature of a building in a hot climate than it is to raise the temperature of a building in a cold climate. In the long run the advantage therefore will possibly lie with the great tropical countries of the world, and one looks now for the construction of very large air-conditioned buildings, wherein work should be more efficiently carried on than it was in the past. Obvious possibilities include the building of a completely air-conditioned unit, such as a University or even a whole city, let us say in India, or indeed in any part of the tropics where natural temperatures and humidity conditions are unfavourable to full physical and mental energy. But the question arises: what are the ideal climatic conditions? Should the temperature be kept the same throughout the year, should it be directly related to temperatures outside, should it vary as between day and night, should it, in other words, simulate the movement of nature as we understand it, providing diurnal differences and annual differences? Should the air be kept dry, or have a constant or a varying degree of moisture? Is it important that the air should be still, or are currents of air desirable?

Although we may claim that air-conditioning is neither necessary nor desirable in Britain, winter heating is certainly required. Yet much of our building construction in this country, especially of ordinary houses, has been of a very hit-and-miss variety.

The position now is that our technicians know more about the insulating qualities of materials at their disposal and of systems of heating and cooling than we do about the conditions we want to create for health and efficiency. Even our hospitals still think there is virtue in large doses of cold damp poison- and smoke-laden air coming through draughty windows. Scientifically it is more likely that no hospital window should be made to open.

This relationship between climate and disease links up with what is now being done in the field of medical geography, the distribution of pests and diseases, not only of human beings but also of animals and of plants throughout the world. Though pests and diseases have been so widely studied by biologists and doctors, little is known in many cases of the details of geographical distribution. Until more is known we are not really in a position to appreciate many of the factors which are operating to make some diseases more prevalent in one place than another. So the linkage of temperature, humidity, and other aspects of climate to health is only one part of the story; the linkage with disease and carriers of disease is another part of the same story. Since this chapter was written I have devoted a small volume to these and related problems – *The Geography of Life and Death*, published by Collins, 1964.

CHAPTER 12

Some Aspects of Rural Land-use Planning

MANY aspects of the use of rural land have already been discussed incidentally in the preceding chapters, but the open countryside has a range of problems peculiarly its own which deserve to be considered as a whole.

Land which is broadly speaking 'open countryside', in which the area occupied by buildings, roads, and other developments directly associated with the habitations of man is relatively small, still occupies about nine-tenths of the surface of Britain. So the description 'rural' can be broadly applied to nine-tenths of the land, 'urban' to one-tenth. Official statistics would have us believe that rather over 80 per cent of our population is urban, leaving nearly 20 per cent rural. But for purposes of those statistics all those residing in a rural district are classed as rural. One has only to remember that, at the 1951 Census, Epsom Rural District, to quote one London example, covered the populous dormitory area of Ashtead, or that the railway employees of the great Didcot works were 'rural', to realize that those who actually live in the country are far less than 20 per cent. Calculations which were made for the Scott Report of the total population living in isolated farms and cottages, in hamlets and villages, suggest that roughly one-tenth of our people should properly be classed as rural, against nine-tenths as urban.

Thus we have nine-tenths of the people living on one-tenth of the land in towns. The remaining one-tenth not only live in the country, but because they live there they are automatically the custodians of the national estate. It is they who keep, make, or mar the countryside for the town-dweller's benefit or otherwise. The duality of function of the country dweller is often overlooked by townsman and countryman alike. In a democracy it follows that nine-tenths of the electorate are basically urban-minded in the sense that they know the problems of the countryside from

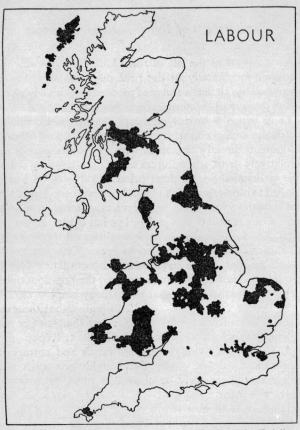

LABOUR

Fig. 25. The geography of the 1955 General Election – the Socialism of the towns. The pattern of the 1959 Election is essentially the same

observation rather than from daily personal experience. In Britain the dangers inherent in this position are avoided to some extent by the electoral divisions of the country – there is both reason and right in the existence of rural constitu-

encies often of huge extent but small populations, side by
side with urban constituencies of small extent but large

Fig. 26. The geography of the 1955 General Election – the Conserva-
tive rural areas. Except for North Devon (Liberal) the 1959 changes
scarcely show at this scale

populations. How they voted in the General Election of
1955 is a remarkable testimony to the contrast between
rural and urban political views.

No one could truthfully describe the British countryside as monotonous. It is possible to see as much variety of scenery in a trip of twenty-five miles in many parts of this country as one would find in ten times that distance in other lands. We are so used to the infinite variety of our coastline – white chalk cliffs, shingle beaches, marshy flats, sandy strands, craggy rock headlands, all within a few dozen miles, that it is difficult to realize that one can go for 2,000 miles along the eastern seaboard of the United States without finding a single cliff!

The open countryside is equally varied. The fertile parts are closely farmed and occupied by a bewildering mosaic of arable and grass fields with occasional patches of woodland, perhaps some unenclosed common land or a village green, and a few orchards. Down by the rivers liable to flood may be lush meadows separated by ditches or dikes; sweeping over hill areas are the unenclosed rough pastures or moorlands. Whilst, as we have seen, these variations in the rural pattern reflect in the main the influence of relief, soil, and climate, there is a broad zoning associated with the great centres of population and with relative accessibility. Though transport and communications are so good over most of lowland Britain and distances relatively so small that market-gardening and fruit-farming areas are located mainly with reference to soil and local climate, it is common to observe an intensity of farming round some major population centres. Olaf Jonasson postulated a zone of intensive horticulture round cities, together with dairy-farming for milk, giving place at greater distance to mixed farming or arable farming. As distances from consuming centres increase and transport costs rise, so one passes into an outer zone of less intensive land use with much 'ranching' or cattle- and sheep-rearing on open rough grazing and much attention to forestry. In general terms this is true of Britain: north of Aberdeen dairying tends to give place to stock-rearing, and on the western sides of Scotland and Wales favourable soils are less used than they would be if located in areas more accessible from large urban centres.

There is another aspect of this urban influence. The parts of the countryside most intensively used by the townsman are naturally those parts he can reach by bus or local train or his own car on a Saturday afternoon or Sunday. The family man will look for a picnic area within 20 or 25 miles; if he ventures more than 50 miles he faces a tedious crawl back on congested roads which takes away much of the pleasure of the day. If he goes more than 50 miles outwards in a day trip, the sea is most likely the magnet. It follows that there are still large areas of Britain where the open countryside rarely sees the town stranger – except in the holiday months, which are dictated by school holidays as August and the first half of September. Even then certain selected areas receive the bulk of the impact. At this season many farmers derive a welcome addition to income from house guests, often for one-night stays for 'bed and breakfast', and many small towns round the coast have got to make enough money from the visitors to see them through the rest of the year. Many places receive urban visitors to the number of ten times their permanent population in the course of a year: for a famed beauty-spot-cum-curiosity such as Clovelly it may rise to a hundred. The townsman is then so much in the majority that he finds it difficult to believe or remember that there are actually people who *live* in the country or by the sea throughout the year.

Therein perhaps lies the dangerous and harmful idea of a natural antipathy between town and country, or that town planning is something to be contrasted with rural planning, if the latter is required at all. It is vital for the well-being of the nation that the problem of physical planning should be regarded as one whole – as indeed it is under the 1947 Act.

Both townsman and countryman have thus an intimate concern with the future of the countryside, but their viewpoints are frequently different. To the townsman the countryside must seem like a great garden where he can relax and enjoy the freedom which only natural surroundings can bring and where, rather incidentally, crops are grown or meat produced which he may help to consume.

However, since his food normally comes from a shop, and not direct from a farm, it is doubtful whether the consumer is aware of the actual origin of 90 per cent of what he eats. Vaguely the townsman wants to 'preserve' what he enjoys. The picturesque cottage appeals even if it is damp and insanitary (provided he does not have to live in it), the old avenue of trees must be 'preserved' even though each is past its prime and ought to be felled. When the townsman retires to the countryside, provided he has running water and electricity he often welcomes solitude and isolation – which he has deliberately sought.

But what of the countryman – farmer, farm worker, forester – and particularly his wife? Whilst he may and usually does love and enjoy his life and is happy to be really constructively producing, he fails to see why he should not enjoy the advantages of piped water, main drainage, electricity (with consequent radio and TV), and good access. It is because he has not been getting these concomitants of the modern normal standard of living that rural depopulation – made possible in part by mechanization and in still larger measure by easy access to neighbouring towns by car for goods and services previously supplied from the village shop or smithy – has become such a problem.

Uncoordinated Government policy has added to the difficulties. Whilst the policy of not allowing building of houses in the countryside except for farms and farm workers was reversed when it was pointed out that the adventitious dwellers (as described in Chapter 4) were needed to maintain the social structure, it is still unfortunately true that the Ministry of Education is tending to concentrate educational facilities in towns and to close the small village schools which formed such a vital focus of village life in the past. As a result, children in their most formative years are being forced into an urban environment.

An interesting example of contrasted viewpoints came to the fore in 1956–7, when the Government developed, through the Central Electricity Authority, its policy of building nuclear power-stations. Although the element of danger was denied it was decided to locate the stations in remote sites – on the coast because of the need for vast quantities of water and because of certain radioactive elements in the effluent. Bradwell, on the Blackwater estuary in Essex, and a coastal site in Somerset, north of Bridgwater, were two sites selected. In each case there were those local inhabitants, including some farmers, who considered that industry would bring much-needed life to revivify the countryside; others, including other farmers, who saw their already scarce labour being enticed away; but emphatically those who had retired to the country for peace and quiet saw both being destroyed. Some national bodies regretted the destruction of some last remaining sections of rural Britain, others welcomed a better balance of industrial distribution.

The place accorded to agriculture in the national economy is a matter of national policy, and the same is true of the position of forestry and of other uses of the countryside. But there are certain geographical aspects which are relevant. The natural vegetation of most of lowland Britain is deciduous woodland, predominantly of oak, giving place to alder on wet land, birch and Scots pine on light soils, and interrupted by marsh or bog in wet or ill-drained areas. Above the tree line – 1,000 to 1,5000 feet, according to circumstances – open moorland would be natural. The grassland of lowland fields is not natural: it is maintained by man or his grazing animals. The grassland of lowland commons likewise is not natural. Without therefore the constant attention of the farmer all arable and grassland would quickly become covered with a thicket or scrub of bushes such as hawthorn and blackthorn with brambles, bracken, and various coarse growing weeds. In due course this would be invaded by trees and pass eventually, though very slowly, to forest. Deterioration of land often takes place rapidly on land acquired as open spaces by local authorities unaware of the laws of Nature. The cheapest way, indeed the only way, to keep the countryside scenically attractive is to farm it. The services of the farmer to the community in this regard are difficult to assess in money terms, but they are very important.

In the second place, because early after the Great Ice Age Britain was cut off from the Continent, before many trees common on the Continent could establish themselves, it follows that Britain is extremely poor in tree species. The Scots Pine is the only native coniferous tree, and even that is probably only native in Scotland. The oak, birch, alder, beech, and elm are natives, but most of our other favourite trees have been introduced – the spreading chestnut, the sycamore, horse-chestnut, plane, and lime are all introduced, so that the cry against 'exotic' introductions is ill-founded. But Britain is naturally a forested country, and many open moorlands, except at higher levels, owe their origin to centuries of careless exploitation of timber. To re-establish forests is therefore to restore the country more nearly to the aspect it had when Romans or Anglo-Saxons invaded it.

The present policy of reafforestation by the Forestry Commission is thus scientifically well founded. The use of such conifers as Norway Spruce or European Larch is simply introducing into the country trees accidentally kept out after the Ice Age. Sitka Spruce or Douglas Fir are very natural introductions, coming as they do from other regions in the world (western North America) climatically similar to Britain. Afforestation of our poorer lands is thus a natural restoration as well as an economic use.

What size and type of agriculture should we have in Britain? Climate favours grass and fodder crops rather than cereals for grain. Milk and meat are favoured, though animals are poor converters and extravagant of land. Our finest soils, limited in extent, favour the production of fine fruit and vegetables. There are those who would argue that agriculture in Britain should concentrate on local intensive horticulture with extensive ranching elsewhere. But over the centuries a very definite pattern has grown up – a relatively intensive farming based on a rotation of crops, and hence mixed arable-grassland husbandry with careful attention to manuring and soil management which conserves and indeed improves the soil. Such is 'good husbandry' – keeping the land in good heart. The unit over much of the country is the family farm, averaging 100 acres, formerly with the farmer employing several farm workers, now, with mechanization, needing but one. Smaller farms are often part-time or hobby farms.

Rightly or wrongly, present Government policy under

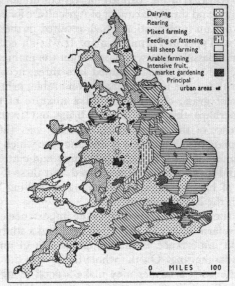

Fig. 27. The main types of farming in England and Wales

the 1947 Agriculture Act is, broadly speaking, to maintain the varied types of mixed farming which as a whole characterize Britain. The farmer is given a guaranteed market at prices fixed in advance for main specified products. In return he is theoretically required to practise good husbandry and is liable to eviction if, after due warnings, he does not; but in practice public opinion is so ranged against what it believes to be unwarranted interference with individual liberties that the provision for eviction is almost a dead letter. So the farmer, with guaranteed prices, ploughing grants and other subsidies, cheap lime and fertilizer, is subsidized by the taxpayer. As a direct consequence the same taxpayer gets much good fresh food, and his national estate is kept in good shape for his enjoyment.

The type of farming practised varies widely from one part of Britain to another. Shortly before the outbreak of the Second World War the Ministry of Agriculture for England and Wales, and the Department of Agriculture for Scotland, carried out an investigation which resulted in the publication of a 'Types of Farming' map. It was an economist's map, and classification was based upon the main source of income, the types being grouped into three, according to whether they were based primarily on arable, primarily on permanent grass, or primarily on a mixture of the two. What perhaps this map fails to bring out is the interdependence of the types, which makes it very difficult to contemplate the elimination of any one type which happens to be 'uneconomic'. Hill-sheep farming and cattle-rearing on upland farms are being subsidized, but these form a reservoir of healthy stock for fattening or adding to dairy herds on the lowland farms.

Reference is made elsewhere to the importance of a well-balanced farm unit, properly equipped, and a study of considerable importance is the mapping of farm units. The result is fascinating. On the whole the poorer the land the larger the unit: a farmer may make a good living on 8 or 10 acres of intensive market garden, but needs 800 or 1,000 of hill grazing if he is to survive as a hill-sheep farmer. The average full-time holding is just under 100 acres, but round towns there is usually a cluster of small holdings: units tend to be larger away from urban centres. Auctioneers make much of a farm in a single block of land surrounded, as they say, by a 'ring fence', but sometimes fragmentation of a holding is essential to secure land of different types. Sometimes a fragmented layout is the result of a division on inheritance, and may be bad. In planning of roads good can be done not only by trying to cause a minimum disturbance of good units, but also by securing a realignment of bad units.

CHAPTER 13

Some Aspects of Urban Geography

WITHIN the last decade or two a whole field of study has grown under the title of urban geography. It is in fact the intensive study of towns and their development in all their geographical aspects. There really are two points of view, or two main fields of study. One is the study of the actual town itself as a settlement, and we can talk in terms of describing and studying townscapes just as we talk of landscapes over a larger area of the countryside. The second study is that of the influence of the town on its surrounding area, sometimes called the hinterland, or latterly the umland. Let us take these two points of view in turn.

Before he can start work in planning for the future the town planner requires factual surveys covering many different aspects of the town. There are normally available large-scale maps or plans which can be used as base maps for special studies. For all settled parts of Britain there are the maps produced by the Ordnance Survey on the scale of 25 inches to the mile, or, strictly, 1 : 2,500. These are survey-accurate in the sense that buildings are shown their proper size, gardens are shown exactly as they are, and roads their true width, but the information does not cover anything like all that which is required by the town planner. It is usual to show private buildings separately from public buildings, and all the more important public buildings are not only shown but named, and the same applies to factories and works. But this information is only a starting point. It is usually necessary to know the distribution of shops as compared with dwellings. In some areas the whole building is devoted to the sale of merchandise. In other cases the shop is restricted to the ground floor, and above it may be either offices or living accommodation. There are various systems of symbols which have been devised so that such details can be clearly shown. We then get a picture of the distribution of shopping facilities in contrast to the distribution of offices or residential accommodation. But the Ordnance Survey map is a map – it does not show things in three dimensions – and heights of buildings, particularly of dwellings, may be important, whether they are bungalows, two-storey or multi-storeyed blocks of flats. Again another map is required. Even these factual details, described and cartographically expressed, may fail to meet the needs of the town planner. Among other problems he is likely to be concerned with overcrowding and the consequent need to provide more living accommodation. Overcrowding is a function of the number of people compared with the number of habitable rooms. The expression 'habitable room', used in a technical town-planning sense, includes bedrooms and living-rooms, but excludes the kitchen (unless it is also used as a living room), bathroom, and offices. A generally accepted definition of overcrowding is more than one person per habitable room.

Naturally the town planner is concerned with future developments, and so a very important field of investigation is the age of buildings. Buildings over a certain age may then be arbitrarily classed as obsolete or obsolescent. It does not require much imagination to see that here there is a possibility of conflict with a judgement based upon historical or aesthetic considerations, especially when another task of the town planner is the recording, for preservation, of buildings of historic interest or architectural merit. Innumerable examples could be given of buildings scheduled for preservation which are at the same time condemned as unfit for habitation.

Houses, shops, and offices, however satisfactory in themselves, do not necessarily add up to a satisfactory town. People demand adequate services, and detailed mapping will often reveal at a glance any inadequacies or difficulties. Separately shown a map of the distribution of post offices, pillar boxes, and telephone kiosks will show how adequately or inadequately Her Majesty's Postmaster-General is serving the town. A map of banks, or a map of butchers' or bakers' shops, serves at once two functions – it shows the adequacy of the existing service and at the same time suggests where there are possibilities for new enterprise.

It is of interest to note that towns appear to show opposing trends in development. In some there is, with growth, an increasing concentration of facilities in what is commonly called in America the C.B.D. or central business district,

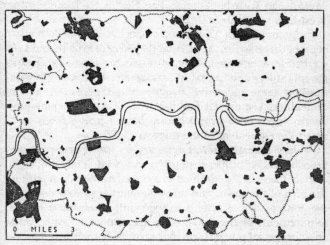

Fig. 28. The open spaces of the London area. The technique used in this simple map of showing just one feature is a very helpful one. In this case the parts of London County with few open spaces at once leap to the eye

with its department stores, wide range of specialist shops, restaurants, and places of entertainment. Here one finds all one needs if not under one roof at least within a few yards – but one must make the journey from home to reach the centre. In a way the opposite is the concept of the 'neighbourhood unit', where at least the usual daily needs can all be satisfied in the immediate neighbourhood of the home. Most of the larger cities begin to show a further differentiation – into a centre where the functions of administration, business, wholesale and retail distribution, amusement, and catering occupy separate areas, and into the residential areas each with local shopping and servicing facilities. In the majority of large cities different trades definitely congregate together, as if inviting competition. Londoners are very familiar with this differentiation. Whitehall is synonymous in our minds with central government, as Harley Street is with specialists in the medical field, or Charing Cross Road with bookshops. The City is for business, the West End for pleasure.

Professor Griffith Taylor and others have worked out concepts of the growth of towns and the effect of growth and age on their form or morphology. He distinguishes such stages as the infantile, adult or mature, and senile. Towns do not pass through these successive stages without many attendant difficulties. We are all familiar with worn-out neighbourhoods where once proud houses have become slums and await the equivalent of the surgeon's knife.

A very special interest attaches to the concept of the neighbourhood units previously mentioned. They are, as it were, villages, self-contained to a considerable extent within the area of the town, and town-planners tend to encourage the concept of the neighbourhood unit where most of the requirements of the inhabitants are obtained locally, and only for special purposes do they go outside their neighbourhood to the big stores, or to the theatre or restaurants. Students who have studied the townscapes of Birmingham have pointed out that one can almost distinguish a neighbourhood unit by the presence of a Woolworth's, a bank, and a post office supported by a number of individual shops catering for the essential requirements of life such as radio and television. An earlier manifestation of the same phenomena is the grouping of communities around their church and their chapel, so that one had and, notably in Wales, still has neighbourhood units based on a place of worship.

The concept of the neighbourhood unit and its mapping is important in its relationship to lines of communication. It is almost essential that there should be a school in a neighbourhood unit and the children going to the school should not be required to cross a main road. Hence when the town is being expanded and neighbourhood units deliberately created, relationship to traffic and traffic flow is of vital importance. We get a further development in these days with the idea of certain shopping streets being closed to vehicular traffic. This is one of the concepts brought to the fore in certain of our new towns.

Quite a different aspect of town study is in connexion with those old centres which are places of pilgrimage because of their historic buildings. We think in terms of the great cathedral cities where the interest does not centre on the cathedral alone, but spreads to the cathedral precincts and to the many attractive legacies from the past which give a distinctive 'flavour' to towns and cities in Britain. Here there is need for accurate mapping and recording of details not only of buildings which are definitely scheduled because of their historical interest, but also of many others of less individual significance. This is recognized in our modern planning legislation by listing of ancient monuments and buildings of special architectural or historic interest for which Building Preservation Orders may be made. Such buildings may not be materially altered by the owners without necessary permission. Unfortunately there is nothing to prevent an impecunious or uninterested owner from allowing such property to fall to pieces.

We now turn to the town in relationship to the country by which it is surrounded. Many towns have an obvious function: the county towns, which house the administration responsible for conducting affairs of the county, is an obvious case, and we are familiar with the idea of the county town as a market centre for an agricultural neighbourhood. Many of our towns actually grew up in the past to serve the countryside in this way.

An important geographical concept is that of the hinterland. The word is of German origin and was used to denote the land *behind* a port from which produce is collected for export through the port and into which goods imported into the port are distributed. An unsuccessful attempt was made

to anglicize the word as 'hinderland', but the implied connexion with 'hinder' rather than 'behind' caused it to be
dropped. In broad general terms it may be clear what area
is included in the hinterland of a port. Where, for example,
the port is backed by high mountains across which neither

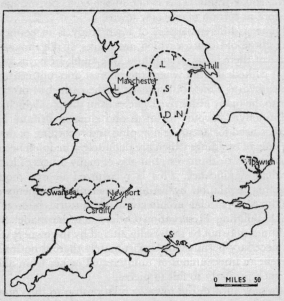

Fig. 29. The concept of the port hinterland. Whilst the larger ports
such as London and Liverpool serve the *whole* country, the *bulk* of the
trade of Manchester, Hull, Swansea, Newport and Cardiff, and Ipswich
is within the areas of hinterlands marked for each

road nor rail passes, the limits may be defined with considerable precision. Akyab in Burma may be quoted as an
example, but such simple cases are increasingly rare though
the hinterland of a port on an island such as Stornoway in
the Outer Hebrides is commonly limited to the island or
island group. When one attempts to delimit the hinterland
of a mainland port one finds it varies with the commodity,
can be changed by alteration in freight rates, and that its

boundaries are quite indefinite. In Britain some of our smaller ports may have a definite hinterland to which they distribute coal received by water, but for other purposes lie in the hinterlands of larger ports. In many cases it is true to say that the whole of Britain lies in the hinterland of one of the major ports. London and Liverpool draw goods for export from all parts of the country: tea received in London is distributed to the whole country.

Notwithstanding these difficulties of interpretation, there is an area, however vague, whose economic life is closely

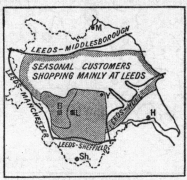

Fig. 30. An early attempt to delimit the 'umland' of Leeds–Bradford

bound up with that of a major urban centre. In this sense the term 'hinterland' has been extended in use to apply not only to ports but also to inland centres. Sometimes this is referred to as an urban hinterland or zone of influence, or the term of German origin, 'umland', is used. The definition and delimitation of an umland becomes actually a matter of definite practical importance in commerce and industry. In practice a large manufacturer whose products are in wide demand must decide for himself his centres for distribution and the umland which each must serve. Conversely, if he is using local raw materials he must decide his centres and the umland from which each draws – as in the case of sugar-beet factories or milk-processing centres. The smaller manufacturer who relies on public transport for distribution of his products, especially if those products are perishable or must be regularly delivered, is very much concerned with the

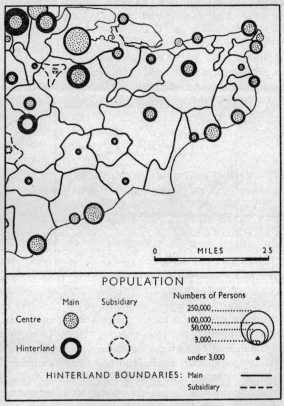

Fig. 31. The hinterlands of market towns in south-eastern England

limit which by accident or design the authorities set for the urban hinterland. Local train and bus services in particular serve to delimit the area served by an urban centre, and from which the town draws its customers. The local newspaper may be limited in circulation in this way: effective delivery from a retailer may depend almost entirely on the parcels services provided. As the motor bus has come so largely to replace all other forms of public transport, local bus services have come more and more to delimit urban hinterlands. Pioneer studies in this field were carried out by Mr F. H. W. Green, and one of the maps published in the National Planning Series on the scale of 1 : 625,000 or about 10 miles to 1 inch shows the result of his work.

Obviously the delimitation of an urban hinterland is important in planning. It shows the area for which a town must provide certain services: it shows the area (and the consequent population) which can be drawn upon to support a new enterprise be it private or public. Indeed, a manufacturer would call much of such investigation market research.

The network of agricultural markets over the country tells much the same story, and illustrates the ever-changing character of the pattern. In the old days, when people walked to market and drove their animals on foot, markets had to be closely spaced. Four miles apart was an average distance for markets handling stock, rather more where produce such as corn could easily be taken by cart and horse. The development of motor transport has widened the sphere of influence of a market, with the result that many small markets have disappeared and the villages or towns where they were situated have declined in relative importance unless they have been revivified by some new activity – a small factory or two, the attraction of a cinema, or the provision of a modern school or an effective service station and repair shop. The towns may have declined in actual population as well as importance. The problem of the decaying country town is often to be added to that of rural depopulation.

Unfortunately in the haste of development since the Industrial Revolution many of our towns are far from the attractive places for living they might be. They have become what must be regarded as a blot on the landscape rather than the reverse. This applies particularly to some of the

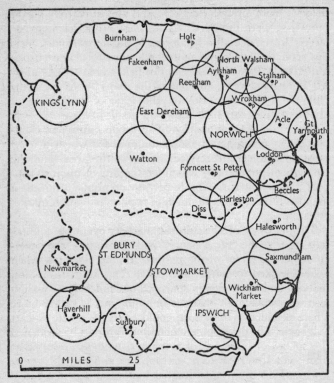

Fig. 32. The agricultural markets of East Anglia, 1958. Each market centre is surrounded by a circle of 6 miles radius

industrial towns where there is a great creation of smoke and dirt. In recent years, with an increase in our standard of living, we have become conscious of the evil of slum dwellings, whether the slum dwellings are in the town or in the country. We are now becoming conscious of the evil of smoke, and surveys have been carried out to show the way in which given towns give rise to a 'smoke area' according to the drift of air currents. This is a new investigation. Not only are unpleasant living conditions caused by soot and smoke, but with some factories there is an additional trouble resulting from dangerous fumes. This was one of the early troubles of the great chemical works at Billingham, where housing on the immediate leeward side of fume-producing chimneys was found to suffer from a very rapid destruction of metal windows – in fact some houses actually had to be abandoned for this reason.

Techniques have been devised for the survey of smoky areas which are a prelude to the creation, now undertaken by quite a number of towns, of smokeless zones. Contrary to popular belief, the small individual household chimney has not been quite as much the villain of the piece as we have believed in the past; but there is no doubt that we should benefit greatly by the development of district heating, and the elimination of the individual fire unless there is careful control of the smoke which is produced therefrom.

Finally there are certain other relationships between a town and its hinterland which need to be considered. One is recreational: the mapping and calculation of acreages of public and private open spaces within the urban area and in the surrounding country with the object of determining whether a green belt is required.

Still another aspect of town–country relationship is in regard to local administration.

During the Second World War, when there was a possibility of the invasion of this country, it was necessary to divide it up into Civil Defence Regions, each of which, if necessary, could carry on a government of its own, if other parts of the country were occupied by enemy forces. These Civil Defence Regions, ten in number, began to assume other uses, and we were left when the war ended with the division of the country into what were virtually provinces, something new to peacetime Britain. It is true that each of the Government Departments determined the area, extent, as well as the capital of its province or its region from its own point of view, and the Treasury were not very successful in laying down the standard regions which are shown in the accompanying map.

Several questions arise. First, what is the natural division of the country so that each region holds together with some homogeneity? Secondly, what is the suitable capital to choose for each region? There are certain cases which are

Fig. 33. 'Standard regions' of England and Wales

more or less obvious: Birmingham and the West Midland Region, five counties, have fitted very well together. Much more difficult is the straggling area of the south-west. Should the regional capital be, as it actually is for most purposes, at Bristol? Should it be more centrally placed, for example at Exeter; or should a larger centre, such as Plymouth, be chosen? Obviously there are many different

172

considerations. There is the access from the capital, from London, to the regional capital; another, perhaps more important, is the accessibility of different parts of the region from its regional capital. Bristol offers a bad example in the South-western Region, where British Railways make absolutely no attempt whatsoever to improve rail communications between the old Southern area – that is to say, north Devon and Cornwall, and the regional capital. A somewhat similar problem arises in East Anglia. Is the natural capital Norwich, which is rather ex-centrally placed, or is it better located in Cambridge? It would at least seem clear that the multiplicity of divisions of the country consequent upon autonomous decisions of Government departments is far from being a satisfactory arrangement. The recent trend has been towards the elimination of the region as an administrative unit.

We may at this stage refer to another and a very important aspect which is applicable not only to towns and their hinterlands but also to much of the work of applied geography discussed throughout this book. That is the importance of looking at the whole question from the historical point of view; seeing what has happened in the past; tracing for example the growth, development, and changing character, function, and morphology of towns from the past right up to the present day. This is not only a matter of historical interest; one finds there are trends in development, leading from the past to the present. The presumption is that trends obvious at the present time which have been established over the past will be continued into the future unless positive action is taken to change them. It may almost be said that planning – positive, physical planning – is one of two things. It is either encouragement of a trend which is believed on policy grounds to be good, or it is the attempted reversal of a trend which is believed to be bad. For example, the concentration of industry and population which was taking place in the inter-war years in the neighbourhood of Greater London and Greater Birmingham was regarded by the Barlow Commission and subsequently by the Government

seen in the deliberate selection of sites and the establishment of new towns and the selection of small centres for
expansion. This involves giving practical expression to
theories that are often little more than hunches: that people

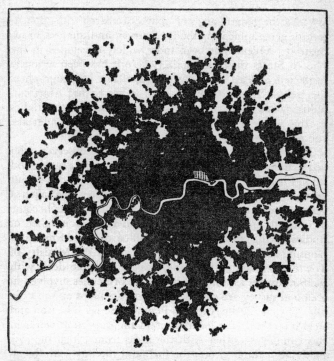

Fig. 35. London in 1945 on the same scale of Figure 34. The black parts
are built-up areas

prefer living in houses with gardens rather than flats with
ground managed for them; that they like being near
(though not too near) their work; that spaciousness of layout is preferable to cosiness. A reaction is seen in an attempt
to study the successful towns rather than pathological cases,
and to find the scientific basis of successful urbanism.

CHAPTER 14

Some Aspects of Industrial Geography

UNDER the general aegis of 'market research' the application of geographical methods of survey and analysis to industrial problems has been more widely developed in the United States than in Britain, where it has been seriously neglected at least by industrialists, if not by geographers themselves. It would indeed be true to say that American industrialists regularly pay large sums of money for studies in this field, which academic workers here undertake voluntarily and have difficulty in getting published.

The first approach is that of the outside observer, who takes either a specific industry or an industrial region, and studies it objectively in its geographical aspects. Of recent years, when the Government of this country has taken a very active part in the location of industry, it has become incumbent upon officialdom to undertake a number of studies of this sort. The Maps Office of the Ministry of Housing and Local Government, formerly the Ministry of Town and Country Planning, has for example dealt with such industries as iron and steel. The principles involved in a factual survey are clearly shown on the maps on the scale of 1 : 625,000 in the National Planning Series. The iron and steel map shows the location of all the important works in this country, together with the areas from which the raw materials – the iron ore, the fuel, and the flux – are being obtained. This is the usual first stage: the study and mapping of location, together with an indication of the relative size of the units which have been studied. The second stage is normally the endeavour to interpret the reasons for the existing distribution pattern. It is here that one must attempt to assess the relative pull of such factors in the location as raw materials, power supplies, transport facilities, labour, and markets. A geographer tends to think in terms of the actual

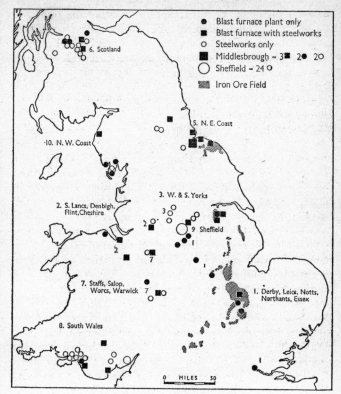

Fig. 36. The iron and steel industry of Britain. The British Iron and Steel Federation distinguishes nine regions, numbered 1 to 9

location of resources in each of these categories; an economist would be more likely to translate the actual location into terms of a secondary factor such as transport costs, but broadly speaking the principle is the same. In the case quoted – the iron and steel industry – there are certain outstanding characteristics: the raw materials are all heavy and bulky and of relatively low value; the final product is also heavy and bulky. With high-grade iron ore the bulk and weight of the waste material are relatively small; with the low-grade iron ores which are extensively used from the Jurassic and other sedimentary rocks of central England, where the percentage of iron in the ore is only between 20 and 30, there is a great deal of waste material. It is quite obvious why, in the first instance of high-quality iron ore, the broad tendency is to take the iron ore to the source of fuel – that is, to the coalfields – whereas with the change to the use of the lower-grade ores the tendency has been for the establishment of Scunthorpes and Corbys located at the source of the iron ore, and to bring the necessary fuel and other materials to those centres. Other things being equal, cheap and easy transporting away of the products, pig-iron, steel in the form of joists, rails, and so on, is a very important consideration. Obviously water transport is very advantageous in this regard where any question of export is concerned. In such an industry as iron and steel, where there are now a relatively small number of units, it is possible to analyse the reasons for the existence of each and reveal interesting examples of varying policy. The Ebbw Valley Steelworks were expanded in the inter-war years to counteract the then seriously prevailing unemployment in South Wales. The policy then was to take the industry to the reservoir of labour, quite independently of the fact that the location of the plant in one of the narrow valleys of Wales did not offer very good facilities for the layout of the plant, for the receipt of the raw materials, or for the export of the finished products. Here providing work for an existing labour force was the chief consideration. The establishment of the giant steel-rolling mills at Margam near Port Talbot after the war is a very interesting example of the influence which is still exercised by geographical factors. For modern steel-rolling mills there was a need for a considerable area of relatively flat land afforded by the marshland along the coast. There was need for the raw material to be easily available – because of the waterside location, this could be brought readily by sea. For fuel there was the nearby South

Wales coalfield; for labour a reservoir provided by Swansea, Port Talbot, and other urban centres in South Wales. This site is an almost ideal example of the paramount influence of the geographical factors combined with others, including labour and particularly the availability of suitable transport facilities. Similar locational advantages are seen at the great Llanwern steel mills near Newport, opened in 1962.

In studying individual industries and individual industrial plants it is vitally important to select what may be regarded as good examples of their type: successful. Our tendency is rather the reverse: to study pathological cases, those which for some reason or other are not satisfactory, and to try to find out the reasons for their lack of success. This applies equally well to a whole range of urban and industrial studies. It is important, for example, that we should investigate not only the conditions of slums which require to be removed, but also the conditions in towns where there is apparent happiness and prosperity, and see what factors have led to those good conditions – quite a different point of view. It is only when the Government departments concerned have studied the factors which have led to the successful prosecution of an industry that they can say yes or no to lines of development proposed by the industries concerned.

In the Scott Report an effort was made to classify industries, starting from the extractive, which are tied to the occurrence of the mineral which is being won, passing through the heavy, which again are tied to a very considerable extent to a small number of localities, to other groups, ending up with those industries which are both light and easily mobile, having few demands upon raw materials. The tendency in the last-mentioned is to choose location relative to markets, or perhaps to a labour supply. Though there are some light industries which can be located more or less at will – that is to say, can be subject to locational planning – the number which can thus be planned in accordance with national policy is far more limited than one is apt to think at first sight. Certain industries which apparently are easily mobile are found to have special requirements, such as an enormous demand upon water – hence water supply is a limiting factor. Others are found to have noxious effluent, hence the difficulty of getting rid of a vast quantity of polluted water. This applies to the new atomic-power stations where there is a slight radio-active character to the waste and great care must be taken in disposing of it. With other industries there is an element of danger – for example, the making of fireworks – or an element of noxious character, such as the smell associated with tanning. Many of the heavy industries, already tied by raw materials, are still further restricted for these reasons. The cement industry, with its dust, apart from its fumes, is a good example. There is a whole range of industries which deal with heavy chemicals, including the refining of oil, which have certain noxious characteristics, including fumes and smell, which are accordingly best located away from areas of human settlement – that is to say, from residential areas. Our oil refineries have thus been established on tidal water, essential because of the receipt of the crude oil by tankers from all over the world, but in practically every case at a distance from residential areas. It is a pity that in the past we did not take the same precautions with regard to the gasworks which disfigure and lower the rateable value in contiguous areas in so many of the towns and cities throughout Britain.

We have referred earlier to the fact that in an old-settled country such as Britain, the rural pattern was really determined many centuries ago. In something the same way our industrial pattern was determined by the Industrial Revolution, when there was the natural tendency for industry to settle itself on the coalfields. As industry expanded there was a marked regional specialization; so we have the association of a large part of Lancashire with the cotton industry, the West Riding of Yorkshire with the woollen industry. What one finds now is that these old-established locations exercise a pull and have an influence on the continuance of the industry. One may refer to this as geographical inertia, or, if one prefers to take a more positive view, geographical momentum. From either point of view there is undoubtedly a great tendency for industrial areas which have become established to continue and to grow, though it may be that there is now no longer any direct dependence on formerly important physical factors. The classical example is afforded by those industries which depended originally on the motive power of moving water, used directly. The cutlery industry of Sheffield is often quoted in this regard; the streams were dammed up and provided a head of water for the working of the forges and hammers, and a local stone provided excellent grindstones. These factors have long since ceased to have any influence – neither the water power nor the grindstones are used – and today Sheffield in a way struggles against the difficult relief of the narrow valleys which converge on the Don in that area. But geographical momentum is such that it has gone ahead and become as it is today, the great centre of the cutlery industry, not only in Britain but of the world as a whole. Other places have been less fortunate, and the once-flourishing woollen industry of East Anglia, relying on the wool of local sheep, has disappeared, and has given place to the woollen industry of West Riding.

What may be called historical accidents have similarly a continuing influence. The chance settlement of Flemish silk-weavers, immigrant refugees to this country at Spitalfields in London and later in Coventry, gave rise to the great silk industry so long associated with those centres. Often the evolution of an industry can clearly be related to the existence of a labour pool. There is some truth in the case which is often quoted, namely that of Coventry, where the Flemish silk-weavers settled because it was a town free from guild restrictions. Coventry was long famous for its silk ribbons. There was the need of the fine machinery for making these, and naturally there grew up, as has so often been the case, side by side with a textile industry, the industry for the manufacture and supply of the appropriate machinery. A tradition of fine machinery work expanded in due course into the making of sewing machines, and then, with the

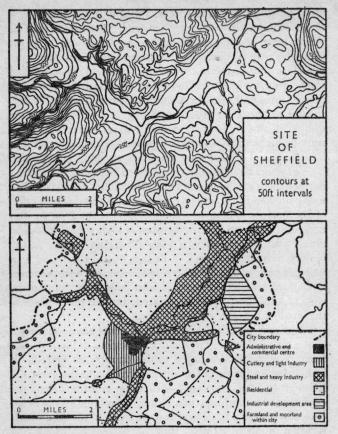

Fig. 37. The site of Sheffield and the modern differentiation of the city into functional zones

coming of the bicycle age, into the manufacture of bicycles, to be followed by motor-cycles, then by cars, and still later by aircraft. It may be said, then, that indirectly over the course of time the aircraft industry of Coventry is the direct result of the settlement in the non-Guild town of Flemish

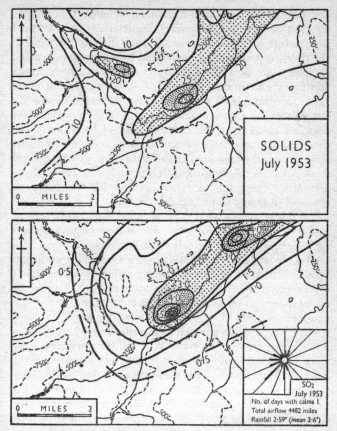

Fig. 38. Atmospheric pollution around Sheffield

silk-weavers. The mention of the association of the textile industries with textile machinery is a reminder of a linkage which is very common in industrial areas. When studying an industrial area as distinct from a separate industry, one finds the advantages which often accrue to manufacturers in locating their works, including new works, in areas where

183

there is already a range of industries of comparable character. Whilst some industries are characterized by a vertical integration, so that all processes from the raw material to the finished product are carried out by one vast unit, other industries are dependent on small specialist units concentrating on one process, all closely linked together. Birmingham, for example, is well known for its linked industries. Sometimes it is a question not of comparable but of complementary character. The establishment of light textile industries, such as clothing manufactures, in dockyard towns is a very good example of this. Portsmouth may be quoted as such a case, where work is thus provided for the womenfolk when their husbands are away with the Navy or engaged in heavy work in the dockyards.

All this relates to what may be called the outside view of industry and industrial areas. We turn now to a second approach, which may be called the inside view.

It is obvious that in planning the location of his works the industrialist must consider the many different factors which are involved. Perhaps in the majority of cases it is still an *ad hoc* investigation which is carried out by the Board of the company concerned, or experts whom they employ for this specific purpose. This is well seen in the case where there is a deliberate move of an established industry to a new location. The decision of Fords in Britain to move from Trafford Park in Manchester, with its restricted area, to the then peculiar site – for so it was regarded by their many competitors – at Dagenham on the Thames in Essex is a very interesting case in point. Nowhere in the south was there any blast-furnace or steel mills upon which the Ford works were to be based. But Dagenham had many advantages. There was proximity to the continental market, deep tidewater, plenty of room for expansion, enormous potential market in London, near at hand, as well as a potential labour supply in the neighbourhood – all such things were considered in detail. The oil companies, in choosing their refinery sites on the lower Thames-side, were attracted by the same advantages. In the Stamp Memorial Lecture for

1956 an interesting example was given of the way in which international corporations chose their headquarters, and where such factors as relative cost of living, taxation, and currency regulations are as vital in the selection of administrative centres as the supply of raw materials may be for their works.

The third point of view is again what may be called an internal point of view, but it is that of an industry thinking in terms of its markets. That which is commonly known as market research is to a large extent a case of applied geography with an emphasis on the potential buying power of different areas. A recent American book called the *Economic Geography of Industrial Materials* is a symposium prepared by some thirty-two authors, nearly all of whom are leading members of their trade organizations. Each author enumerates the factors which an industrialist must consider in siting a new works. In a world of severe competition a false move may mean financial ruin. Where, for example, are the people going to be living in 1965? Where will they have the most purchasing power for this commodity or that? A growing concentration of population must clearly be regarded as a powerful incentive to the construction of industrial works designed to supply a local market with consumer goods.

Although reference is made in this chapter to industry, and one thinks in terms of manufacturing industry, the general principles we are discussing apply in many branches of trade and commerce. Particularly concerned are those who supply goods and services to growing communities. There is no doubt that the retailer, such as Woolworth's and the other great chain-stores of this world, look very carefully at the various factors here involved. The provision of banking facilities is in the same position. An interesting example of what may be called rather specialized 'market research' is afforded by the expert advice which is sought by certain of the great insurance companies. This has become developed much more in the United States than it has in Britain. Let us take an insurance company which is insuring against damage by hail, flood, lightning, tempest, and so on. The hurricanes which originate in the West Indies and over the tropical seas of the Caribbean and make their way northwards along the coasts of Florida or into the heart of the United States tend to follow definite paths, so that there are certain lines in the United States which are more liable to damage from these disasters than others. Similarly, the incidence of hail, which may be seriously destructive, tends to follow definite tracts. It is only when the company concerned employs an expert meteorologist that it is able to quote competitive rates on insurance in any given locality. Even in Britain it is in fact ridiculous to pretend that a single overall insurance rate for dangers of damage by tempest and flood is fair when some areas are so much more liable to these than others. Here is a case where the physical geographer is in a position to give an assessment, after careful examination, on the possible dangers in any given area. Little such work is done at the present time. Industrialists often work in the dark. The actual lack of knowledge was shown by the British Government's rationing of fuel. Geographically it is colder in winter in the east and warmer in the west, but the allocation of fuel was more in the north than the south, which was simply grossly unfair. There is no doubt that lucrative fields lie ahead for the trained expert in applied geography, and there is no doubt also that many manufacturing firms can save themselves part of the losses which they may have suffered in the past through the application to their particular problems of some of the lines of research indicated in this chapter.

CHAPTER 15

Some Geographical Aspects of Trade

IT is perhaps almost impossible to separate the geographical aspects of trade and transportation from the geographical aspects of industry which we looked at briefly in the preceding chapter. Once again the broad principles are the same. There is first the systematic objective mapping of the facts concerned. The trader will wish to know the distribution of his customers. When these are shown in map form there are often peculiarities in the pattern which call for explanation. Is it because in one area he has a good agent that he is securing the bulk of his orders from there? Is it because his advertising in the local Press is effective in one area and not in another? What are the things to be explained? Another aspect of almost daily occurrence is with retail trade: how efficient is the servicing of different localities? It is sometimes apparent to the eye, but more often needs specific study to show that some areas are over-supplied, others under-supplied with one particular group of commodities, and that the opportunity exists for those willing or able to repair the deficiencies. Many of the big firms of course undertake research of this sort. An interesting recent development is that of mobile shops, returning to the old days when the trader went round with his horse and cart and his range of goods to country villages. Such mobile shops yield data of potential retail markets before heavy capital expenditure is incurred.

In the international sphere there are many aspects where the application of geographical methods of survey and analysis are certainly most desirable. In these days barriers of various sorts have been raised between nation and nation. There are currency restrictions, there are restrictions due to customs and tariffs. It is possible to show cartographically the existence, size, and character of these barriers between the nations. From another point of view it would be of great interest to have cartographical representations of the spread of modern economic empires. The growth of the dollar empire is something quite fantastic when seen on a map of the world. Or again, what would a map of the world look like when designed to show the ramifications of one of the large oil combines? What again would be the appearance of a map of the world showing the extent of Coca-Colonization, as it has been called? There exists a great Coca-Cola Empire with just here and there a few pockets of resistance.

Apart from these international aspects of trade, there are many investigations of the type discussed in the preceding chapter which may be described as marketing research. It is often urged that British exporters do not study sufficiently the markets of the world to which their goods may be going. To the resident in the overseas countries concerned, a lot of conditions become so much a part of his everyday life that he fails to realize that they may be completely unknown to the people at home. A very interesting example of that is the ignorance in Britain of climatic conditions in different parts of the world, and what those climatic conditions involve in the adjustment of everyday habits and life to them. We are all familiar with some of the old and well-worn examples of the ignorance which one country has of another. We recall the story of the Lords of the Admiralty chartering ships during the First World War to take sand to Egypt to fill the sandbags. And I well recall my early days in Burma, where I was Professor of Geography in the University of Rangoon, and when both my wife and I took out to that country many things which we thought would be useful. We had failed to realize that almost anything which had a constituent of gum or glue to keep it together would soon disintegrate in the hot, damp Rangoon climate. I remember to this day the jewel boxes which fell to pieces, the shoes which disintegrated, the sequins on dresses which melted, the bindings on books with their tasty glue which provided such a remarkable attraction to cockroaches and other tropical insects. I soon learned why sheets of stamps cannot be de-

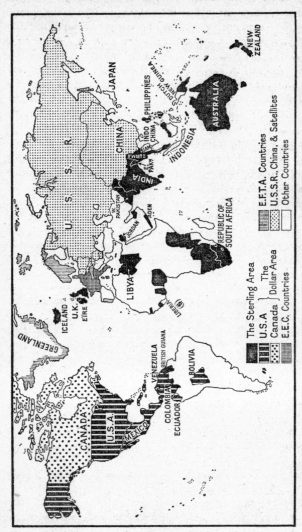

Fig. 39. The currency regions of the world. (From *Chisholm's Handbook of Commercial Geography*, Longmans.)

livered to post offices unless their gummed surfaces are separated by waxed paper. My wife soon learned that certain fabrics which were perfectly satisfactory at home were completely useless in the tropics. When affected by the different rate of perspiration from the body they very quickly became wet and correspondingly transparent.

There is no doubt that every year even now millions of pounds are being lost by simple ignorance of such things as climatic conditions in different parts of the world. It is no use exporting to countries commodities which may be useful enough in Britain but which do not suit either the natural or the indoor climate of the countries concerned. Take the case of Canada and the United States, where the artificial climate maintained inside the houses of temperatures between 75° and 80° F. makes completely unsuitable the clothing which would be most useful in Europe. It is perhaps unkind to drag into this consideration the famous failure of the groundnut scheme in Africa. But there is not the slightest doubt that this colossal loss of between £30 and £40 million was primarily due to a lack of survey of the geographical conditions prevailing, whether it was the natural soil conditions, the climatic conditions, the character of the vegetation, or still more the reasons for the spasmodic distribution of the tiny patches of cultivation which led to an entirely false assessment concerning the fertility of the land as a whole. There is no doubt that all the way through this disastrous scheme there were tragedies. I do not know how true it is that certain secondhand machinery, taken at great expense to the interior of East Africa, was on arrival identified as machinery for the removal of barnacles from ships, but there is no doubt that all over the world examples can be given of the consequences of neglecting the ordinary methods of geographical survey.

The trade of the world travels along certain main lines of communication or trade routes; comparatively little is spasmodic. There is an interesting field of studies here: the measurement and delineation of the flow of traffic. We have seen the necessity of this in determining the traffic requirements of British roads. It is certainly just as important to measure the flow of traffic along the international ocean highways of the world. It has become important in recent years in connexion with air routes, and all this is likely to increase. The difficulties are not unlike those encountered on a small scale within the confines of Britain: it is easy to make a *post mortem*, far more difficult to translate the experience of the past into planning for the future.

CHAPTER 16

Conclusions

IT is now over 150 years since Robert Malthus shocked the world of his time by his *Essay on Population*. His gloomy prognostications did not materialize and were almost forgotten for a century. He pointed out that the world's population increased in geometrical ratio, and in due course it would fill to overflowing the fixed land surface of the world on which the output of food increased only in arithmetical ratio. When he wrote, in the latter part of the eighteenth century, the vast new lands of the world – Australia, much of South America, and most of the prairies of North America – were unknown, and with the enormous expansion which took place in the nineteenth century it seemed that the natural checks which he saw – famine, pestilence – on this growth of population were scarcely to be seriously considered. But in this present day and age the effect of death control all over the world, through the spread of knowledge of medicine and development of hygiene and health services, is to prevent the former heavy toll of life through infant and maternal mortality and to keep alive the people to an ever-increasing age. Medical skill, through inoculation, virtually prevents the very existence of the plagues and scourges which from time to time decimated whole nations. The knowledge and practice of death control have spread more rapidly than the knowledge and practice of birth control, with the result that the world's population is increasing at a rate greater than ever before, and so is pressing more and more seriously on resources of the land. It is obvious why studies should be more and more directed towards demography and the study of population as such, its phenomena of growth and development. It stresses the necessity for the mapping of population distribution discussed in this book, the mapping of population movements, the mapping of population growth, so that we may see quite clearly the factual position. As in so many other cases, sentiment, or it may be some particular political or social view, is apt to warp the judgement of the man in the street as well as that of the leaders of nations, and it is vitally important that the factual position should be kept to the fore.

Taking the other half of the picture – the land – it is not surprising that there should be a rapidly increasing interest in the land and its resources. We talk glibly now in terms of resource conservation, we talk of the potential of land, we talk, too, of the planning of land. Again it is the factual position which we need to know, and it is nearly always the case that we find that the actual information available is totally inadequate. We have, for example, no measure at the present time of the use which man actually makes of the land in most parts of the world. How can we plan for the future until we know the present position, and the reasons for that present position? There are those who are in a great hurry to make the world a better place in the future, and who want to skip the lessons which history can teach us, who want to skip the lessons which we can derive from what is happening at the present day, and who like to think in terms of land potential, and entirely of planning for the future, treating the surface of the earth as if it were a blank sheet of paper in an architect's drawing office.

Yet we know that the present distribution of population on the surface of the earth, and the present use which is made of the land and its resources, are due to the action and interaction of a whole series of factors: the geographical factors, which we have stressed in this book, the historical factors, the social and economic factors have all of them played their part in determining the present position. They are factors which will go on influencing us in the future, and the question is therefore: how can we possibly plan for the future until we objectively and scientifically study all the factors which have been so important up to the present day? Our studies should reveal the trends and, as we have said earlier, planning for the future is either the encouragement of existing trends where they are believed to be for the benefit of mankind, or the prevention of the further development of trends which are believed to be bad. At every stage we come to realize the importance and significance of having Nature on our side, of working with Nature wherever possible.

In the highly competitive world in which we find ourselves today, with almost every nation on earth regarding it as a sign of maturity that it should develop its own manufactures, a country like Britain, which depends on the extension of its manufacturing industries and the maintenance of its export trade, must clearly give its industries in the future every possible advantage. This means seeking the factors which are advantageous. We find this in the location of industry, that industry cannot be located at a planner's will. From some particular social or aesthetic point of view the planner may indicate an industrial site, but unless in choosing such a location the physical and natural factors are operating on the side of the industrialist and resulting in the maintenance of low costs, efficient production, and efficient distribution, the effect of planning will be disaster. We can go so far as to say that in the world as it is constituted at the present day the natural geographical factors are more important than they have ever been in the past. Man has not emancipated himself from the influence of those factors. It is true he may know more and more how to control them, but their influence is there, and is going to remain in a way which we cannot escape.

It should have become apparent to the reader of this book that the geographer has an important function to perform which in a way is complementary to that which is already performed by the statistician. The statistician, with his firm basic knowledge of the science of mathematics, applies his mathematical knowledge to the interpretation, analysis, and synthesis of facts and figures which relate to a very wide variety of human affairs. The geographer is concerned primarily with the cartographical analysis. The well-known old adage that the map is the tool of the geographer remains essentially true, but it is a tool which he should use also for the enlightenment of his fellows and to assist in the progress of the human race. Distributions which he shows on his maps often show irregularities which cry out for explanation and determination of the operative factors which must be understood before any remedial measures can be taken. It may be asked, why has so little of this work, comparatively speaking, been undertaken in the past? The answer is probably that whilst the making and use of maps have been known for millennia, and have been vital in those spheres which for so long occupied the attention of mankind, the waging of wars, and the developing of campaigns and the expansion of empires, it is only in comparatively recent years that the application of mapping to other purposes has come to be properly studied at a university level and to be applied. It is tragically true that under the stresses of war, when even existence is threatened, research and new developments are stimulated. Our own Ordnance Survey originated when there was the fear of the invasion of Britain by Napoleon and it was realized that we had no adequate maps of the country. Our Ministry of Agriculture dates from the same time and circumstances; when it was feared that our food supplies would be in danger through the invasion of Napoleon, we set up in 1793 the Board of Agriculture and Internal Improvement, which in due course became our Ministry of Agriculture. At the end of the First World War the delegations which met at Versailles to plan a world in which there should never again be such a conflict, displayed a colossal ignorance of the simple geographical factors which were so vital to their deliberations. It is even said that a considerable portion of one session was wasted because of the discussion as to the future of Georgia. One group was thinking of the Georgia now part of the U.S.S.R., the other group was thinking of the Georgia which forms a State of the U.S.A. It was not until some time passed that there was an appreciation that the discussion was really revolving about two entirely different parts of the world. Be that as it may, the ten years which followed the end of the First World War saw the establishment in practically every University in the British Isles of full Honours Departments of Geography, which should remove in the future the stigma of such ignorance from a growing number of our population.

The development of air transport and rapid communication between one part of the world during and since the Second World War has naturally led to this, the present, being christened the Air Age. It has given a new slant to map study as concerned with air travel; the use of great circle routes across the Pole has caused us to look at the world from a new angle, and to construct new maps for the purpose. Far more important than this is the need to understand, in a way in which we have never understood before, what this earth holds for us, and how we should develop its resources by their careful conservation. And so it is that the field of applied geography has in fact grown up since the Second World War as a vital part of our equipment for the study of the future and as our guide to future developments.

So far as I know, this is the first book to be published on Applied Geography – along the lines of a course I gave at the London School of Economics for the three years before my retirement in 1958. For the two years, 1956–7 and 1957–8, I shared that course with my colleague, Mr Robert C. Estall, and I am greatly indebted to him for having read through the first rough draft of this book and for having offered many valuable comments.

In the circumstances it would be strange if I had been able to do more than indicate some of the lines of study and some of the aims and methods as they apply to this country. I am conscious of the many omissions, the many cases of quite inadequate treatment, perhaps the many half-truths; but if I have done something to stimulate interest I shall have achieved my object.

Some Notes on Further Reading

NOTES ON FURTHER READING

In response to a number of requests a few notes are here added to assist those whose interest has been aroused and who would like to pursue further some aspects of applied geography. Since the first edition of this book was published only a few months ago there has appeared the first full-length book covering almost the same field – but in French. Curiously enough, geographical methods have been less applied to practical problems in France than in many other countries, and so Professor Michel Phlipponneau in *Géographie et Action: Introduction à la géographie appliquée* (Paris: Armand Colin, 1960, 19 NF) seeks to enlighten his fellow countrymen by recounting what has been done in other lands, and so gives a good account of applied geography in the Soviet countries, western Europe, and elsewhere, before enlarging on many of the topics studied here.

To those whose basic knowledge of geography is slight, I would commend E. W. H. Briault and J. H. Hubbard's *An Introduction to Advanced Geography* (London: Longmans, 1957). Written primarily for sixth forms, it leaves the reader with a stimulating sense of how much there is still to be learnt.

Turning to those primarily interested in the British Isles, I have attempted in two volumes to trace the evolution of the present scene. In the first, *Britain's Structure and Scenery* (London: Collins New Naturalist Library, 4th ed., 1955; now available in Collins Fontana Library, 1960 at 7s. 6d.) – how the varied scenery of the present day is linked with a long and complex history evolving slowly through the millions of years of geological time. In the second (*Man and the Land*, same series, 1955) I have taken that knowledge for granted and traced the hand of man in the growth of the humanized landscape. The background of factual knowledge for the British Isles will be found in L. D. Stamp and S. H. Beaver, *The British Isles: A Geographic and Economic*

Survey (London: Longmans, 5th ed., 1963, 50s.), which may be supplemented by *Great Britain: Geographical Essays* (Cambridge University Press, 1962, 42s.), which deals with the country on a basis of regions, edited by Jean Mitchell.

The rapidly increasing pressure of population on land resources all over the world is now attracting attention everywhere, and this has resulted in a spate of books. In my own *Our Developing World* (London: Faber, 1960, 18s.) I have tried to present an unbiased picture: the facts are very largely those collected by United Nations and published in the *Demographic Yearbook* and by Food and Agriculture Organization and published in *The Yearbook of Food and Agricultural Statistics* and a range of other publications.

A full account of the Land Utilisation Survey of Britain and its findings – the interpretation of the land-use patterns (Chapters 5, 6, and 7), leading on to land planning, will be found in *The Land and Britain; Its Use and Misuse* (London: Longmans, 3rd ed., 1962, 90s.), whilst the details for all the counties of England, Wales, and Scotland will be found analysed by numerous experts in the 92 parts (nine volumes) of *The Land of Britain* – some out of print, but to be consulted in most University libraries. The difficult problem of the classification of land (Chapter 8) is considered in part in the works already quoted (*The Land of Britain* and *Our Developing World*) and some of the problems which emerge in G. P. Wibberley, *Agriculture and Urban Growth* (London: Michael Joseph, 1960). Others are studied by R. H. Best and J. T. Coppock, *The Changing Use of Land in Britain* (London: Faber, 1962, 42s.).

It was during the Second World War that thinking people in this country became conscious of the particular problem which would arise once the war was over – how to secure from a small fixed area of only an acre per head all that a nation of over 50,000,000 people would need in industrial expansion, better housing, space for recreation, improved roads, and facilities for air travel, whilst maintaining the right land for production of food and raw materials, notably timber. Nor could the claims of the fighting services for training grounds be ignored, and what provision could be made to provide refuges in perpetuity for our native fauna and flora. What was hailed at the time as the 'blue print' for the countryside was the *Report of the Committee on Land Utilization in Rural Areas* (H.M.S.O., 1942). This Report can still be read with profit: from it stemmed others on National Parks, Nature Conservancy, Footpaths and Access, all of which have led in turn to the legislation which has given us comprehensive Town and Country Planning, National Parks, and Nature Reserves. The National Parks Commission issues an annual report; in 1960 the Nature Conservancy summarized in an attractive brochure its first ten years of work.

The late Sir Patrick Abercrombie had a lively appreciation of the geographical factors in town and country planning; many of the magnificently produced 'Plans' which he prepared, alone or with others, deserve study – especially the *County of London* (London: Macmillan, 1943), *Greater London* (H.M.S.O., 1944), *Plymouth* and *Hull*, and others. The West Midland Group produced an interesting study entitled *English County* dealing with Herefordshire (London: Faber, 1946, 21*s.*) and a study of Greater Birmingham entitled *Conurbation* (London: Architectural Press, 1948). Other noteworthy plans were those for Merseyside, Manchester, Edinburgh, and such studies as *County Town* (Worcester) (London: Murray, 1946) and *Devon and Cornwall* by a Survey Committee of the University College of Exeter (Exeter: Wheaton, 1947). All these are pioneer works, and the spirit behind them is exemplified in the writings of Thomas Sharp – especially *Town and Countryside* (O.U.P., 1932). Now it is incumbent upon every county to produce both county and town plans – each with descriptive text, based upon a special survey. A broader viewpoint is apparent in fine studies such as *A Survey of Whitby*, edited by G. H. J. Daysh (Eton: Shakespeare Head Press, 1958, £3 3*s.*), and studies by Daysh on Tyneside and West Cumberland.

A problem of special import where geography and planning meet is our varied British coastline, and J. A. Steers,

The Coastline of England and Wales (Cambridge University Press), is invaluable. As an example of a still unsolved problem the *Report of the Royal Commission on Common Lands* (H.M.S.O., Cmd. 462, 1958, 14s.) should be noted. The problem has been discussed for the general reader by W. G. Hoskins and L. D. Stamp, *The Common Lands of England and Wales* (London: Collins New Naturalist Series, 1963, 25s.).

Turning to the wider field, much of the ground covered in this book would be considered 'Conservation' in America, and the literature is vast. Recommended for reference rather than reading is the 1,200-page tome entitled *Man's Role in Changing the Face of the Earth*, the result of an international symposium, edited by W. L. Thomas (University of Chicago Press, 1956). Many of the American books deal entirely or primarily with American conditions – vast land resources – and the best are *Conservation of Natural Resources*, edited by G.-H. Smith (New York: Wiley, 2nd ed., 1958) and M. Clawson, R. B. Held, and C. H. Stoddard, *Land for the Future* (Baltimore: Johns Hopkins Press; London: O.U.P., 1960). It is interesting to have a practical view from a South African angle in R. C. Haw, *The Conservation of Natural Resources* (London: Faber, 1959, 30s.). What is being called Medical Geography – the geographical distribution of human disease and the factors involved – is attracting much attention. *A National Atlas of Diseases*, edited by G. Melvyn Howe, is published by the Royal Geographical Society and Nelson (1963), and there are also *Some Aspects of Medical Geography* by L. D. Stamp (The Heath Clark Lectures; London: O.U.P., 1964) and *The Geography of Life and Death*, by L. D. Stamp (Collins, 1964).

In the more strictly geographical field the series edited by S. W. Wooldridge and W. G. East in Hutchinson's University Library may be cordially recommended, especially *The Spirit and Purpose of Geography*, by the Editors; *The Geography of Towns*, by A. E. Smailes; *Railways and Geography*, by A. C. O'Dell; *Geography and Planning*, by T. W. Freeman; the *Geography of Air Transport*, by K. R. Sealy; *The Port of London*, by J. Bird. Among other volumes of Collins New

Naturalist Series than those already mentioned is the very important *Climate and the British Scene*, by Gordon Manley.

It has been urged in this book that the geographical approach is closely identified with the cartographical representation of data. To some, map-making comes naturally, but all can profit by such a practical guide as F. J. Monkhouse and H. R. Wilkinson, *Maps and Diagrams* (London: Methuen, 1952). It raises the question why some maps are successful, others are not.

In recent years there has been a tremendous upsurge in the appreciation of the geographical point of view, and the number of books now published in the field is enormous. It is interesting that a pioneer like *Chisholm's Handbook of Commercial Geography*, first published in 1889 and reaching its 17th Edition in 1962, still retains its popularity as a standard work of reference (London: Longmans, 80s.). A wide range of regional books is contained in Methuen's Advanced Geographies, and a growing one in Longmans Geographies for Advanced Study. Britain has still no counterpart of the great *Géographie Universelle* in twenty-three large quarto volumes.

The autumn of 1963 was marked by the publication of a magnificent work of reference, the *Atlas of Britain and Northern Ireland*, edited by D. P. Bickmore and M. A. Shaw (O.U.P.) which covers almost every aspect of British resources at the mid-century.

INDEX

Index

*Some more books published by Penguins
are described on the
following pages*

METALS IN THE SERVICE OF MAN

W. Alexander and A. Street

Metals in the Service of Man is a fascinating record, illustrated with photographs and diagrams, of the part played in life and civilization by the many metals in common use. It will make clear to even the most bewildered reader the qualities and peculiarities of molybdenum, tungsten, titanium, tellurium, and their fellows. Few technical terms are used, and those few are carefully defined for the unscientific reader.

It opens with an analysis of the earth's crust, and an explanation as to how we get our metals. Next the alloying of various metals is discussed, after which other chapters deal with metals under the microscope and their inner structure. Later sections are concerned with the shaping of metals, corrosion, methods of joining metals, and possible future developments.

'A credit to both authors and publishers. ... We have no hesitation in recommending this book to the many who handle metals in their daily work; even metallurgists will find its perusal a welcome change from textbooks' – *Metallurgia*

'The book is written in a most attractive and often humorous style and technical terms are used as sparingly as possible' – *Engineering*

GEOGRAPHY OF WORLD AFFAIRS

J. P. Cole

Day after day more and more places are mentioned in the newspapers, on the radio, and on television. It may be possible to follow world affairs and world problems without knowing anything about Queen Maud Land or Okinawa, Rwanda and Burundi or Surinam, but few people have more than a vague impression even of such important places as Formosa, Turkey, or Venezuela. The main purpose of this book is to help the reader who is not a specialist in geography to find his way about the world and to provide him with facts about the location, population, size, and activities of the more important countries in it. Most of the material in this book is geographical in nature, but many questions cannot be considered, even from a purely geographical viewpoint, without reference to history, politics, and economics.

GEOLOGY AND SCENERY IN
ENGLAND AND WALES

A. E. Trueman

Scenery depends on land structure – in other words, its geology. Everyone interested in the countryside, how it has taken shape, why it presents us with the varied beauties of mountain and moorland, river valley and fertile meadow, is, if often unconsciously, appreciating its geology.

Sir Arthur Trueman's book – first issued in 1938 as *The Scenery of England and Wales* and later reprinted in revised form as a Pelican book – makes it abundantly clear that geology is preeminently a layman's science. The author believes that the geologist acquires an eye for country and an understanding of nature not excelled by that of the artist or the poet.

The English and Welsh countryside is considered district by district, each chapter dealing with one type of country – the Cotswold Stone belt, the Chalk lands, the Pennine Moors, the Lake District, and so on. The reader already familiar with the areas dealt with will learn to view them in a new light, while those who seek information about the peculiar features and delights of localities yet unknown to them will be amply rewarded. The author began to write it while himself on holiday, and has kept the needs of other holiday-makers prominently in mind.

There are 95 illustrations and diagrams, specially drawn to illustrate the text.

THE FACE OF THE EARTH

G. H. Dury

The young natural science of geomorphology – the study of the form of the ground – is much less forbidding than its name. It is developing fast, and already promises to achieve some independence both of geology and of physical geography. In this book a professional geomorphologist tells how this field of knowledge is advancing, examines some of the hotly-disputed problems which have to be solved, and discusses the processes by which construction and erosion affect the physical landscape. Among the topics receiving attention are the weakening of rocks by weathering, their removal by the forces of erosion, the cyclic development of the land-surface, the evolution of river-systems, the effects of volcanic action and of glaciers, and the surface forms of deserts.

In choosing his examples, the author has been able to select freely from the results of his own field work. There are 102 diagrams in the text and 48 pages of plates.

For a complete list of books available please write to Penguin Books whose address can be found on the back of the title page